AVIATION
A Complete Legal Guide

"The first flight lasted only twelve seconds, a flight very modest when compared with that of birds, but it was, nevertheless, the first in the history of the world in which a machine carrying a man had raised itself by its own power into the air in free flight, had sailed forward on a level course without reduction in speed, and had finally landed without being wrecked."

—The Wright brothers' description of the first powered flight at Kitty Hawk, NC

AVIATION

A Complete Legal Guide

Cliff Roberson, LLM, Ph.D

TAB BOOKS Inc.
Blue Ridge Summit, PA 17214

FIRST EDITION
FIRST PRINTING

Library of Congress Cataloging in Publication Data

Roberson, Cliff, 1937-
Aviation : a complete legal guide.

Includes index.
1. Aeronautics—Law and legislation—United States—
Popular works. I. Title.
KF2400.Z9R59 1987 343.73'097 87-10194
ISBN 0-8306-9414-5
ISBN 0-8306-2414-7 (pbk.)

Questions regarding the content of this book
should be addressed to:

Reader Inquiry Branch
Editorial Department
TAB BOOKS Inc.
P.O. Box 40
Blue Ridge Summit, PA 17214

Contents

Introduction

To some, flying is a sport, a hobby. To others, it is a profession, a business; yet to the majority of both, it's both. This book deals with the complex relationships between aviation and legal issues and problems. The purpose of the book is to provide a clear and concise handbook so that the pilot—novice, experienced, professional, or operator—mechanic, or supply person will have a readable guide on the legal aspects of aviation. It is written in such a way to help you prevent legal problems and/or to lessen the adverse impacts of any legal consequences on aviation-related activities.

The first flight is credited to Orville Wright on December 17, 1903; it was for 120 feet. Since that time, aviation has progressed a long way. As noted earlier, flying is both a recreation and a business. It is a complex activity, and because of the complexity, no one can be associated with aviation long without, in one form or other, considering its legal requirements, problems, duties, and obligations. There are also many government regulations that prescribe when and where you can fly, the types of training required, certificates, etc. There is also constant concern of legal litigation that may arise resulting from aviation-related activities. These concerns and considerations are not new. They were present in 1969, when the *Legal Guide for Pilots and Owners* was first published. That book, updated in 1974, has served its purpose. It is now outdated and is replaced by this text. In addition to replacing the *Legal Guide for Pilots and Owners,* this text has been broadened to take care of concerns of operators, lessors of aircraft, flight instructors, mechanics, and supply persons.

This manual covers all aspects of general aviation law. In considering the choice of topics to be included in this book, an evaluation of possible topics was made to ascertain the proper coverage. In doubtful cases, the decision was made to include the material rather than exclude, enabling a more complete coverage of this complex activity.

A major problem present in presenting this material is doing so in a manner that is appropriate to pilots with varied aviation experience. General aviation pilot experience ranges from students to instrument flight instructors, from the novice mechanic to the chief mechanic. A major goal of this manual is to serve as a legal reference that will be useful to both inexperienced and experienced persons. Accordingly, the manual will remain a valuable resource tool as the individual progresses in aviation experience. To meet the challenge, this text is presented with independent chapters covering each major topic. By using the independent chapter concept, only those chapters that are of concern to the individual reader need be referenced. The independent chapters approach also allows each chapter to be directed to the readers to the level of aviation experience commonly associated with that major topic.

No book can replace the advice of and consultation with an attorney when the need arises. However, a careful reading of this book should inform and enlighten the reader. If it helps prevent a legal problem for a reader, the purchase price is returned with interest.

Throughout this text, I have used many examples of aircraft accidents. The use of these examples enables the reader to obtain a better understanding of the legal principles involved. They are not used to discourage anyone from enjoying the great thrill of general aviation. The safety record of general aviation compares favorably with that of all other forms of transportation, and it's much safer to fly than to drive your car to the airport on a busy freeway.

In the first chapter, I have included a brief summary of the legal aspects of aviation, a discussion on the relationship between state and federal law, and the functions of the Department of Transportation and the National Transportation Safety Board.

Chapter 2 deals with flying license, the power to license, legal requirements, type of license, privileges of license, overcoming legal problems in obtaining a license, medical issues, and individual rights regarding the suspension or revocation of the flying license.

The third chapter is a brief synopsis of the Federal Aviation Administration, its administrative regulations, rule making procedures, exemption procedures, its ability to enforce its rules through the use of criminal offenses and civil sanctions, and a discussion on ferry permits and federal aviation regulations.

Chapter 4 deals with all the aspects of aircraft purchase and registration to include aircraft title, contested ownership of aircraft, aircraft owner responsibilities, aircraft financing, aircraft warranties, passage of title, conditional sales contracts, the release of a conditional sales contract, recording conditional sales contracts, liens, aircraft registrations, certificates of airworthiness, and aircraft records. Chapter 5 contains a discussion on the aircraft maintenance rules.

Chapter 6 covers all aspects of negligence and personal liability. Chapter 7 covers aircraft accidents and investigations; aviation insurance is included in the following chapter. Chapter 9 deals with the control of airspace—the general rules and aircraft traffic considerations and responsibilities.

Chapter 10 is a general discussion regarding state regulations and licensing requirements including the states' ability and rule-making authority.

In Chapter 11, the general considerations, duties, and liabilities of fixed-base operators are considered. Chapter 12 deals with service supply and repair to include duties and responsibilities of mechanics and repair stations.

Chapter 13 covers homebuilts and ultralights. In that chapter, the regulations and general duties and liabilities of persons associated with homebuilts and ultralights are discussed. Chapter 14 discusses the legal responsibilities of flight instructors.

In Chapter 15, flying in foreign countries, such as Mexico, Canada, and the Atlantic "resort" islands, is discussed. Aircraft tax considerations, including the latest (1986) revisions of the federal tax code, are covered in the final chapter. In addition, the manual includes a glossary of the most common legal terms associated with aviation.

Appendix I contains a list of FAA Regional Offices. Appendix II is a reprint of FAR Part 43, which contains the rules regarding maintenance of aircraft. Appendix III is the Advisory Circular AC 20-27C on the certification of amateur-built aircraft. Appendix IV is an Advisory Circular (AC 61-84) which stresses the role of preflight preparation in aviation safety.

Chapter 1

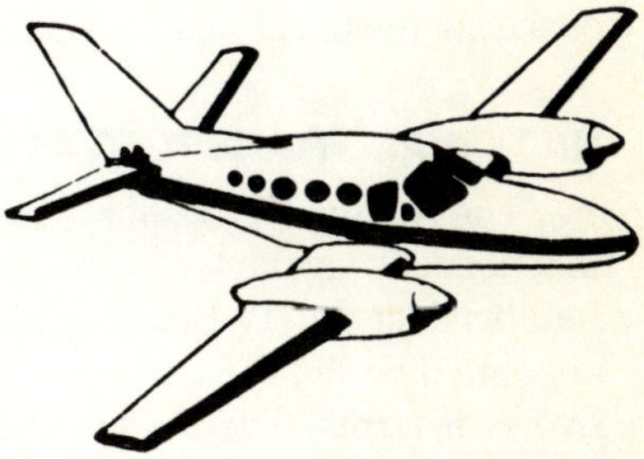

The Law of Flight

"If God had meant you not to fly, he would have given you roots."
—Irv Culver

The major legislation acts that pertain to aviation are:

- ☐ The Air Commerce Act of 1926, which placed the responsibility for providing air safety on the federal government.
- ☐ The Civil Aeronautics Act of 1938, which established the regulatory system for aviation.
- ☐ The Federal Aviation Act of 1958, which mandated federal control of aviation and airspace.
- ☐ The Department of Transportation Act, which established the National Transportation Safety Board and placed FAA under the Department of Transportation.

REGULATORY BODIES

The primary regulatory bodies that govern civil aviation in the United States are the Federal Aviation Administration (discussed in Chapter 3) and the National Transportation Safety Board (discussed later in this chapter).

The Civil Aeronautics Board (CAB) went out of business on January 1, 1985. During its lifetime from 1938 to 1984, it played a significant part in the regulation of aviation. Historically, when it went out of business, it became the first major governmental agency to do so.

In addition to the federal regulations discussed in this book, many phases of aviation are governed by state laws and regulations. Most federal statutes and regulations are based on the power of the federal government to regulate through the "commerce" clause of the U.S. Constitution, which provides that the Congress shall have the right to "regulate commerce among the states." State power to regulate is based normally on two concepts: *police power* and *overriding local concern.* Police power is that power necessary to regulate for the health and safety of the people of the state. Overriding local concern concerns those actions necessary because of local differences.

NATIONAL TRANSPORTATION SAFETY BOARD

The National Transportation Safety Board (NTSB) was established as an independent agency of the federal government in April 1975. By the Independent Safety Board Act of 1975, the board consists of five members appointed by the President and with the advice and consent of the Senate for five year terms. The President designates two of the members as Chair and Vice-Chair of the board for two-year terms. The designation of Chair is required to be approved by the Senate. The purpose of the National Transportation Safety Board is to promote transportation safety by conducting independent investigations of accidents and other safety problems, and formulating safety improvement recommendations.

The board is responsible for investigating, determining accident cause, making safety recommendations, and reporting the facts and circumstances of all U. S. civil aviation accidents; all aircraft accidents in which there is a fatality or substantial property damage, or which involve a passenger train; all pipeline accidents in which there is a fatality or substantial property damage; highway accidents including railroad grade crossing accidents, which the board selects in cooperation with states; major marine casualties, and marine accidents involving public vessels and non-public vessels; and other transportation accidents that are considered catastrophes.

An additional responsibility of the board is to make recommendations pertaining to transportation safety and to act as a catalyst for transportation accident prevention by conducting safety studies, special investigations assessing techniques of accident investigation, and publishing recommended procedures for accident investigation. The board also reviews on appeal the suspension, amendment, modification, revocation, and denial of any certificate or license issued by the Secretary or Administrator of the Department of Safety. The rules pertaining to hearings are discussed in Chapter 7.

Principal Offices

The principal offices of the NTSB are located at 800 Independence Avenue, S.W., Washington, D.C. 20594. The Board also maintains field offices in selected cities.

The National Transportation Safety Board operates a public reference room, which is located in Room 808G at the board's Washington, D.C., headquarters; here, records of inspections or other activities of the board may be inspected by the public. Request for access to any public records on file with the board may be made in person at Room 808G, or by writing the Public Inquiry Section, National Transportation Safety Board, Washington, D.C. 20594, telephone number (202) 382-6735.

The National Transportation Safety Board also makes available a limited number of speakers to discuss subjects relating to the board activity or transportation safety. Requests for speakers should be directed to The National Transportation Board, Office of Government and Public Affairs, Washington, D.C. 20594, telephone (202) 382-6600.

Office of Managing Director

A managing director is appointed by the Board as the executive and administrative head of the Board. The duties of the managing director are to coordinate and direct the activities of the staff. The director is also responsible for the day-to-day operations of the Board, and he recommends and develops plans to achieve the Board's program objectives.

In addition, the Board has delegated to the managing director the below listed functions:

- ☐ The authority to make final determinations as to whether to withhold a Board record from inspection or copying.
- ☐ The approval for publication in the Federal Register notices concerning issuance of accident reports and safety recommendations and responses to safety recommendations as required by the Independent Safety Board Act of 1974.
- ☐ The appointment and supervision of personnel employed by the Board.
- ☐ The distribution of business among such personnel and among organizational components of the Board.
- ☐ The use and expenditure of funds.

Office of Administrative Law Judges

The Office of Administrative Law Judges conducts all formal proceedings under Title VI of the Federal Aviation Act of 1958, as amended. This includes proceedings involving suspension or revocation of certificates and appeals from the actions of the administrator in refusing to issue Airman Certificates. The rules and procedures are discussed in Chapter 3.

Office of General Counsel

The functions of the Office of General Counsel are to provide legal advice and assistance to the Board and its staff components, prepare Board rules, provide opinions, and prepare legal orders for NTSB components. This office also represents the NTSB in court actions in which the Board is a party or is interested in the case.

Office of Accident Investigation

The Bureau of Accident Investigation conducts investigations of all major transportation accidents and other marine, pipeline, and hazardous materials accidents within the Board's jurisdiction; it also recommends the type of hearing to be held, i.e., public or deposition proceedings, to determine the facts, conditions, and circumstances of major accidents. This office also prepares a public report for release by the Board as to the probable cause of each accident and necessary safety modifications or actions to be taken.

Bureau of Field Operations

The Bureau of Field Operations' primary functions are to oversee the Board's field offices located throughout the United States, and conduct aviation, rail, and highway accident investigations within the Board's jurisdiction that are not conducted by the Bureau of Accident Investigation. The Bureau also prepares a public report of accidents investigated by them.

Bureau of Technology

The Bureau of Technology conducts safety studies of specific safety issues and problems, conducts research, and carries out analytical studies and tests on all aspects of the Board's accident investigation, accident prevention, and safety promotion activities. The Bureau also makes safety recommendations and conducts special investigations.

Bureau of Safety Programs

The Bureau of Safety Programs conducts safety programs of specific issues, coordinates the development of and follow-up on safety recommendations issued by the Board, coordinates Board comments on Notices of Proposed Rulemaking by other federal agencies which involve transportation safety issues and provides statistical analyses of transportation accident and incident data.

Go-Team

The Board has on 24-hour alert a "Go-Team." The Go-Team is a group of Board personnel who possess a wide range of accident investigation skills. The team is set to go immediately to a major aviation accident. The team usually arrives at a crash site within hours after the crash and in general usually remains there for seven to ten days for on-site investigations of the accident.

Civil Aeronautics Board (CAB)

The Civil Aeronautics Board (CAB), as noted earlier, was eliminated on January 1, 1985; its functions were either terminated or transferred to the Department of Transportation.

Request For DOT to Investigate Certain Aircraft Accidents

As authorized by Title VII of the Federal Aviation Act of 1958 (as amended in 1966), the NTSB has requested that the Secretary of Transportation investigate certain aircraft accidents. The types of accidents that the Secretary of Transportation (Federal Aviation Administration) investigates include all civil aircraft accidents involving rotorcraft, serial application, amateur-built or restricted category aircraft, and all fixed-wing aircraft which have a certificated maximum gross takeoff weight of 12,500 pounds or less *except:*

- ☐ accidents in which fatal injuries occurred,
- ☐ accidents involving aircraft operated by an air carrier,
- ☐ accidents involving aircraft operated as Air Taxis, and
- ☐ accidents involving midair collisions.

Reports of investigations conducted pursuant to this authority are submitted to the NTSB, from which the Board makes a determination of probable cause. The authority to conduct the investigations does not include the authority to hold public hearings or to determine the probable cause of any accident.

The Board, through its field offices, may assume full responsibility for the investigation of any specific accident that is included in one of the above noted class by notifying the Secretary or designee of the assumption.

The authority for the investigations is given to the Department of Transportation by a notice published in the Federal Register. It is noted that the notice states that this request is necessary because the NTSB does not have sufficient funds to provide adequate facilities and personnel to investigate all accidents involving civil aircraft. The notice also states that it is "temporary in nature and may be modified or terminated by written notice to the Secretary." The notice was published March 1, 1977, and is still in effect.

Chapter 2

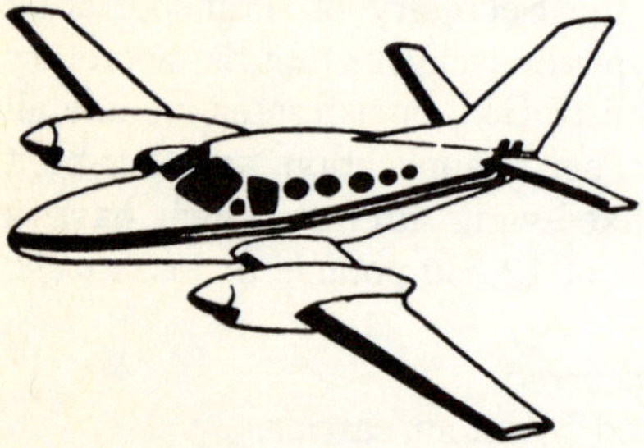

The Flying License

Federal Aviation Regulations Part 61 covers the certification of pilots and flight instructors. In addition, several states also require their citizens to obtain state licenses prior to flying within the state. A non-resident of a state normally cannot be required to obtain a state license in order to fly within that state.

PILOT'S CERTIFICATE

The general rules regarding the obtaining and the operation of an aircraft with a pilot's certificate are:

1. A pilot must have in his/her personal possession a current pilot certificate issued to that pilot when acting as a pilot-in-command or in any other capacity as a required crewmember of a civil aircraft with U.S. registry.

2. No person may act as a pilot-in-command or in any other capacity as a required pilot flight crewmember of an aircraft under a certificate issued to the pilot unless the pilot has a current medical certificate in his/her possession.

3. Only a certified flight instructor may give flight instruction required to qualify for solo flight, solo cross-country, or for the Pilot or Flight Instructor Certificate or rating.

4. No person may operate an airplane as pilot-in-command in weather conditions less than the minimum prescribed for VFR flight unless that person has a current instrument rating.

5. Each person who holds any FAA rating or certificate must present such rating or certificate on request of an FAA representative.

RATINGS AND CERTIFICATES

Before a pilot may operate an airplane as the pilot-in-command, the pilot must have both the required certificate and rating for the airplane. FAA issues the following certificates:

1. Pilot Certificates
   a. Student Pilot
   b. Private Pilot
   c. Commercial Pilot
   d. Airline Transport Pilot
2. Flight Instructor Certificates

FAA places the below ratings on pilot certificates (except for student pilots):

1. Aircraft category ratings
   a. Airplane
   b. Rotorcraft
   c. Glider
   d. Lighter-than-air
2. Airplane class ratings
   a. Single-engine land
   b. Multi-engine land
   c. Single-engine sea
   d. Multi-engine sea
3. Rotorcraft class ratings
   a. Helicopter
   b. Gyroplane
4. Lighter-than-air class ratings
   a. Airship
   b. Free balloon
5. Aircraft type ratings include:
   a. Large aircraft, other than lighter-than-air
   b. Small turbojet-powered airplanes
   c. Small helicopters for operations requiring an airline Pilot Certificate
   d. Other aircraft type ratings specified by the FAA through aircraft type certificate procedures
6. Instrument ratings (for Private and Commercial Pilot Certificates only)
   a. Instrument—Airplanes
   b. Instrument—Helicopter

FAA authorizes the following ratings for Flight Instructor certificates:

1. Aircraft category ratings
   a. Airplane
   b. Rotorcraft
   c. Glider

2. Airplane class ratings
   a. Single-engine
   b. Multi-engine
3. Rotorcraft class ratings
   a. Helicopter
   b. Gyroplane
4. Instrument ratings
   a. Instrument—Airplane
   b. Instrument—Helicopter

Obsolete and no longer valid are free balloon pilot certificates and pilot certificates for rotorcraft, lighter-than-air, helicopter, or autogyro without an associated class rating.

Expiration Dates

Student Pilot Certificates and Flight Instructor Certificates expire at the end of the 24th month after the month in which they were issued, unless renewed. A Category II Pilot authorization (for Instrument Landing System) expires at the end of six months unless renewed. Other pilot certificates are issued without an expiration date.

Medical Certificates

The standards that FAA-designed medical examiners follow were established in 1959. In 1986, the American Medical Association (AMA) finished a two-year review of the standards. The AMA's report suggested some changes, additions, and updates of FAA's medical standards. The recommendations are currently under review. Persons interested in the report may obtain information on it from the Aeromedical Standards Division, FAA, Washington, D.C.20591; telephone (202) 426-3802. If FAA decides to change the standards, they will follow the "proposed rule-making" procedures discussed in Chapter 3.

The duration of medical certificates depends on the type of operations being exercised by the pilot. A First Class Certificate duration is as follows:

☐ For Airline Transport Pilot operations—6 months.
☐ For Commercial Pilot operations—12 months.
☐ For Private Pilot and Student Pilot operations—24 months.

A Second Class Medical Certificate's duration is:

☐ For Commercial Pilot operations—12 months.
☐ For Private Pilot and Student Pilot operations—24 months.

A Third Class Medical Certificate expires at the end of 24 months. Note that for Airline Transport Pilot operations, a First Class Certificate is required; for Commercial Pilot operations, a Second Class Medical Certificate is required.

Replacement of Lost Certificates

A pilot may replace a lost or missing certificate by filing a letter of request with the Department of Transportation, FAA, Airman's Certification Branch, P.O. Box 25082, Oklahoma City, Oklahoma 73215. The letter should contain the following information:

- ☐ Complete name of pilot.
- ☐ Permanent mailing address including zip code.
- ☐ Social Security number.
- ☐ Date and place of birth of certificate holder.
- ☐ Any available information regarding the type, ratings, number, and date of issue of the certificate.

The fee for replacing the certificate should also be included. In 1986, the fee was $2.00.

The application for a lost or destroyed Medical Certificate should be made to the Aeromedical Division of the FAA at the above address. The application should also be accompanied by a check or money order for $2.00 (as of 1986).

In cases where the pilot needs immediate replacement of a lost Medical or Pilot Certificate, the FAA will respond by telegram. This may be applied for by using a prepaid telegram with the above information addressed to the above addresses. The FAA telegram is valid for a period of 60 days. Pilots who use this telegraphic system must also apply by letter for replacement of the lost, missing, or destroyed certificate as noted above, since a permanent certificate will not be issued based on a telegraphic request.

Authorization

A person may not act as the pilot-in-command of any airplane unless that person has both the appropriate certificate and the type rating for that airplane. In certain situations, the FAA may issued an "authorization" to operate a certain airplane in lieu of requiring the rating. Normally this is only issued for ferry flights and flight tests not exceeding 60 days. Prior to issuing an authorization, the FAA must determine that an appropriate level of safety will be achieved during the use of the airplane under the authorization. Only crew members necessary for the flight may be carried on any flight under this provision, and the airplane may not be operated for compensation or hire.

High-Performance Airplanes

For purposes of certificate limitations, high-performance airplanes are defined as airplanes with more than 200 horsepower, or that have retractable landing gear, flaps, and controllable propellers. A pilot with a Private or Commercial Certificate may not operate a high-performance airplane as the pilot-in-command unless that pilot has received flight instruction from an authorized Flight Instructor and the Flight Instructor has certified by logbook entry that the pilot is competent to pilot the subject airplane. An exception to this requirement is made for pilots who have logged pilot-in-command time in high-performance airplanes prior to November 1, 1973.

FLIGHT TESTS

To be eligible to take a flight test, the applicant must:

- ☐ Have passed the required written test since the 24th month before the month in which the flight test will be taken.
- ☐ Have the applicable instruction and aeronautical experience.
- ☐ Hold a current Medical Certificate.
- ☐ Meet the age requirement.
- ☐ Have a written statement from an appropriately certificated flight instructor that the pilot is competent to pass the test based on flight instruction given within the past 60 days.

The need for the written statement is waived for foreign pilots who have a foreign license with at least the same pilot privileges as the pilot is applying for. It is also waived if the pilot is applying for a type rating only, or the pilot is applying for a class rating with an associated type rating.

Retesting after Failure

An applicant who fails a written or flight test may apply for a retest after 30 days, except where the applicant has a written statement from a flight instructor certifying that he (the instructor) has given additional flight or ground instruction and finds the applicant competent to pass the test.

Pilot Logbooks

The required aeronautical training and experience needed to meet the requirements for a certificate or rating must be established by a reliable record. The logging of other flight time is not required. Logbook entries required for each flight are:

- ☐ General—date, total time of flight, place or points of departure and arrival, and type and identification of airplane.
- ☐ Type of training or experience—pilot-in-command or solo, second in command, flight instruction, pilot ground trainer instruction, participating crew, and other pilot time.
- ☐ Conditions of flight—day or night, actual instrument, or simulated instrument conditions.

A student pilot may log as solo time only that time that the pilot is the sole occupant of the airplane or when acting as pilot-in-command of an airplane requiring more than one flight crew member.

Recent Flight Experience

No person may act as pilot-in-command of an aircraft unless the pilot has within the preceding 24 months accomplished a flight review and had his/her logbook endorsed by the instructor. In addition, no pilot may act as pilot-in-command or carry passengers unless the pilot has within the preceding 90 days made three takeoffs and three landings as the sole manipulator of the flight controls. If the airplane is a tailwheel airplane, the landing must have been made to a full stop.

Prior to carrying passengers at night, the pilot must have within the preceding 90 days made at least three takeoffs and landings to a full stop at night in the same category and class of airplane.

Recent instrument flying experience required is six hours of instrument time, either actual or simulated IFR, within the past six months. At least three of the hours must be in the category of aircraft involved.

Falsification of Logbooks

Any fraudulent or intentionally false entry in any logbook that is required to establish or show compliance with any requirement is grounds to refuse—or, if issued, revoke—any certificate or rating.

ALCOHOL AND DRUGS

Recent modifications to FARs provide that no person may act as a crewmember of a civil aircraft:

- ☐ Within eight hours after the consumption of any alcoholic beverage;
- ☐ While under the influence of alcohol;
- ☐ While using any drug that affects the person's faculties in any way contrary to safety; or
- ☐ While having .04 percent by weight or more alcohol in the blood.

Except for emergencies, no pilot-in-command will allow a person who appears to be intoxicated or under the influence of drugs or alcohol to be carried on that aircraft.

The new revision also contains a provision for the testing of pilots. The new regulations state that whenever the Administrator or FAA designee has a reasonable basis to believe that a person may have violated the above restrictions pertaining to alcohol or drugs, that person shall on request by the FAA furnish the FAA the results of a test taken within four hours after acting or attempting to act as a crewmember that indicates percentage by weight of alcohol in the blood or presence of any drug in the body. Furthermore, any information obtained by the FAA as the result of such tests may be evaluated in determining a person's qualifications for any airman's certificate or possible violations of the FARs.

FAR 61.15 provides that conviction of violating any federal or state statute relating to the sale, manufacture, transportation, etc., of narcotic drugs, marijuana, etc., is grounds for denial of a pilot's certificate for a period up to one year after the date of final conviction, or the suspension or revocation of any certificate or rating issued.

Under most situations, a person may appeal the failure to issue, the denial of, or the suspension of a certificate or rating by filing a petition for review with the National Transportation Safety Board (NTSB). For the rules and procedures of hearings before the NTSB, see Chapter 3.

DENIAL OF MEDICAL CERTIFICATE

The authority of the FAA Administrator to issue or deny Medical Certificates has been delegated to the Federal Air Surgeon. Any person who is denied a Medical Certificate by an aviation medical examiner may, within 30 days after the date of the denial, apply in writing and in duplicate to the Federal Air Surgeon, Attention: Chief, Aeromedical Certification Branch, Civil Aeromedical Institute, FAA, P.O. Box 25082, Oklahoma City, Oklahoma 73125 for reconsideration of that denial.

If the individual does not apply for reconsideration during the 30-day period after the date of the denial, the person is considered to have withdrawn his/her application for a Medical Certificate. A denial of the request for reconsideration is considered as a denial that may be subject to proceedings pursuant to the Federal Aviation Act (i.e., petition to NTSB).

Chapter 3

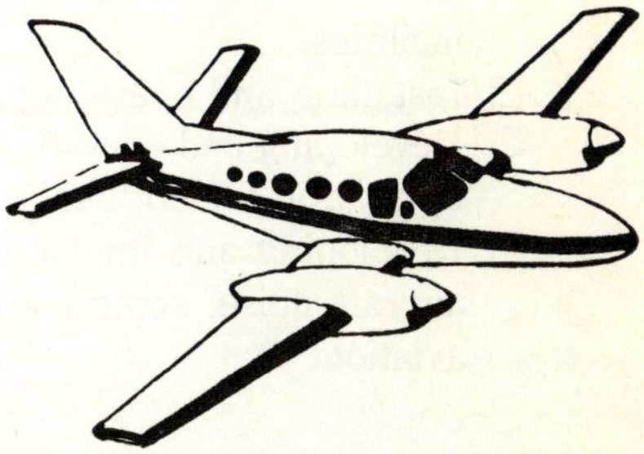

The Federal Aviation Administration

The Federal Aviation Administration (originally the Federal Aviation Agency) was established by the Federal Aviation Act of 1958, and became a part of the department of Transportation in 1967 pursuant to a reorganization of the Department of Transportation.

The FAA can trace its history back to the Air Commerce Act of 1926. That act established the Aeronautics Branch in the Department of Commerce with the authority to issue pilot and aircraft certificates. In addition, the Branch had the duties of promoting flying safety and issuing flight information. Later, it was reorganized as the Bureau of Air Commerce. The Civil Aeronautics Act of 1938 established the Civil Aeronautics Authority (CAA) as an independent entity with the responsibilities formerly assigned to the Bureau of Air Commerce.

In 1940, the CAA was again reorganized as the Civil Aeronautics Administration within the Department of Commerce and a semi-independent Civil Aeronautics Board (CAB) was established. The CAB had administrative ties with the Department of Commerce, but reported directly to Congress. The CAB was abolished in 1985. As noted above, the Federal Aviation Agency was established in 1958. In 1967, the Federal Aviation Agency was made a part of the Department of Transportation and became the Federal Aviation Administration.

The functions and activities of the Federal Aviation Administration are:

- ☐ Regulating air commerce in a manner that promotes development and safety and fulfills the requirements of national defense;

- ☐ Controlling the use of navigable airspace of the United States and regulating both civil and military operations in such airspace in the interest of safety and efficiency;
- ☐ Promoting, encouraging, and developing civil aeronautics;
- ☐ Consolidating research and development with respect to air navigation facilities;
- ☐ Installing and operating air navigation facilities;
- ☐ Developing and operating a common system of air traffic control and navigation for both civil and military aircraft; and
- ☐ Developing and implementing programs and regulations to control aircraft noise, sonic boom, and other environmental effects of civil aviation.

SAFETY REGULATIONS

The FAA administrator issues and enforces rules, regulations, and minimum standards relating to the manufacture, operation, and maintenance of aircraft, as well as the rating and certification (including medical) of pilots and the certification of airports. The FAA also performs flight inspection of air navigation facilities in the U.S. In 1986, there were over 800,000 pilots with FAA certificates and over 400,000 other airmen with various types of certification.

For a discussion of aircraft investigation functions of the FAA, see Chapter 6.

AIRSPACE AND AIR TRAFFIC MANAGEMENT

To perform its function of airspace and air traffic management, the FAA operates Airport Traffic Control Towers, Air Route Traffic Control Centers, and Flight Service Stations. In addition, it develops air traffic rules and regulations and allocates the use of airspace. Almost half of FAA's workforce of approximately 50,000 persons are engaged in some phase of air traffic control. Presently, FAA operates over 400 Airport Control Towers, 23 Air Route Traffic Control Centers, and over 300 Flight Service Stations.

AIR NAVIGATION FACILITIES

The FAA is responsible for the location, construction, maintenance, and operation of visual and electronic aids to air navigation. In so doing, the FAA operates and maintains voice/data communications equipment, radar facilities, computer systems, and visual display equipment at Flight Service Stations, Air Traffic Control Towers, and Air Route Traffic Control Centers. To maintain this equipment, FAA employs approximately 10,000 technicians and engineers. As of 1986, there were 275 long-range Terminal Radar Systems, more than 800 Instrument Landing Systems, and approximately 950 very-high frequency omnidirectional radio ranges.

RESEARCH AND DEVELOPMENT

The research and development activities of the FAA are directed toward providing systems procedures and facilities needed for the safe and efficient system of air navigation and air traffic control to meet both the needs of civil aviation and the inter-defense system. The agency also performs aeromedical research to apply knowledge gained from its research program and research programs of others to the safety and promotion of civil aviation. The FAA also supports development testing of aircraft, engines, propellers, and appliances. Much of the FAA's research and development efforts are done at the FAA's Technical Center at Atlantic City, NJ; the Transportation Systems Center at Cambridge, MA; and FAA's Civil Aeromedical Institute at Oklahoma City, OK.

AIRPORT PROGRAMS

The FAA maintains a national plan of airport requirements, and administers grant programs for the development of public use airports. It also develops standards and technical guidance on airport planning, designs, safety operations, and provides grants to assist public agencies in the airport system in master planning for airport development and improvements.

As of 1986, there were approximately 16,000 airports in the United States; only about 5,000 are publicly owned. Only 5,200 have paved runways and only 4,800 have lighted runways. During the period from Fiscal Years 1982-1987, the FAA, under the Airport Improvement Program, was allotted over $5 billion in funds for airport planning and construction projects to improve airports in the U.S.

METROPOLITAN WASHINGTON AIRPORTS

The FAA is also responsible for the care, operation, and maintenance improvement of Dulles and National Airports in Washington, D.C. It serves as airport proprietor for both Washington Metropolitan airports. The FAA also operates the public-use airport at its Technical Center, Atlantic City, NJ.

REGISTRATION AND RECORDING

The FAA is responsible for operating a system of aircraft registration and the recording of documents affecting title or interest in aircraft, aircraft engines, propellers, appliances, and spare parts. In 1986, there were over 200,000 civil aircraft registered with the FAA.

Under the FAA Act of 1958, FAA is responsible for promoting aviation safety and civil aviation abroad by the exchange of aeronautical information with foreign aviation authorities, certifying foreign entities as repair stations, foreign airmen, mechanics, negotiating bilateral airworthiness agreements to facilitate the import and export of aircraft and components, and providing technical assistance and training in all areas of the FAA's expertise. The FAA also provides technical representation at international conferences including participation in the International Civil Aviation Organization.

MISCELLANEOUS PROGRAMS

The FAA also administers the aviation insurance and loan guarantee programs. It is an allotting agency under the defense material system with respect to the priorities and allocations of civil aircraft and civil aircraft operations. The FAA develops specifications for the preparation of aeronautical charts. It publishes current information on airways and airport service and issues technical publications for the improvement of safety in flight, airport planning and design, and other aeronautical activities. For a list of the major field organizations of the Federal Aviation Administration, see Appendix A.

CONSUMER HOTLINE

In 1986, the FAA established a consumer hotline. Its purpose is to offer consumers a convenient source for information on such matters as child safety seats, airport security, and FAA services such as examinations, aircraft certification, and facility operations.

Individuals calling the FAA consumer hotline (1-800-FAA-SURE) should receive a return call from an appropriate FAA official. The hotline will not respond to airline "service" problems such as lost luggage or flight cancellations. Consumers who are still dissatisfied may contact the Office of Intergovernmental and Consumer Affairs in the Department of Transportation. The telephone number is (202) 755-2220. The hotline is operational throughout the United States except Alaska.

RULE MAKING PROCEDURES

Normally, a rule is issued, changed, or cancelled on the initiative of the FAA or by petition (request) from any interested person. Any pilot or owner may submit a request to the FAA to issue, amend, or cancel a rule.

When a petition submitted by a pilot or owner is received, a determination is first made as to whether it merits full consideration by the FAA. If, in the opinion of the Administrator, no action is deemed necessary, then the person who submitted the petition is notified that no action will be taken or that the requested rule action is denied.

However, should FAA decide that the petition discloses adequate reasons or that the proposed rule will promote safety, the FAA Administrator will issue a Notice of Proposed Rule Making. In special cases where immediate action is required, the Administrator may adopt a final rule. However, this action is restricted to emergency situations. In most cases, the rules or modification to the rules are originated by a person within the FAA.

A Notice of Proposed Rule Making (NPRM) is then published in the Federal Register, unless all persons concerned with the rule can be mailed a copy of it. The purpose of publishing is to give interested parties an opportunity to state their views on proposed rules or modifications to rules.

Interested persons may obtain a copy of a specific NPRM that has been published in the Federal Register by writing to the Federal Aviation Administration, Office of Public Affairs, Attention: Public Inquiry Center, APA-430 800 Independence Avenue Southwest, Washington, D.C. 20591. The request should cite the docket number, notice number, or other reference such as title, FAR Part number, and date published in the Federal Register to help identify the specific NPRM desired.

Persons who have a continuing interest in certain FARs and who wish to receive all of the NPRMs that apply to those FARs may avail themselves of NPRM mailing list service. This service provides for automatic mailing of NPRMs following publication in the Federal Register. There is no charge for this service. Interested persons to be placed on the mailing list should submit a request to the U.S. Department of Transportation, Distribution Requirement Section, M-494.1, Washington, D.C. 20590. The letter or postcard requesting entry on the mailing list should clearly show title or name, company or organization, street address, city, state, and zip code. The FAA recommends the use of title rather than a name where the addressee is affiliated with a company, association, university, state agency, etc.

Any pilot or owner wishing to submit a petition to adopt, change, or cancel a rule, or who desires to voice his opinion on a proposed rule should mail a written statement of the fact to the FAA. In cases where there will be a public hearing, personal attendance is a method of voicing an opinion on the rule under consideration. If there is a public hearing, it will be contained in the Notice of Proposed Rule Making.

The FAA is not immune to public opinion. For example, one year, the FAA announced a proposed rule change concerning the establishment of two classes of Private Pilot Certificates. A factor in the FAA's decision not to adopt the proposed rule was the number of protests received from private pilots.

There is no requirement that the petition or request be a formal legal document. However, it should be legible and identify the rule in question, or state the proposed rule being requested. Experience would seem to indicate that typed responses personally signed by the responder are more effective than handwritten ones or those produced in bulk quantity. In addition, the statement should contain any information or argument available to support your views. The pilot or owner should also state his/her interest in the action. The written statement should be mailed in duplicate to the Federal Aviation Administration, 800 Independence Avenue Southwest, Washington, D.C. 20591--unless a different address is given in the NPRM.

If, after evaluation of the information, views, and arguments submitted upon a proposed rule, the FAA determines that the rule should be adopted, a notice of this decision is published in the Federal Register. Likewise, when the decision is that the rule should not be adopted, a notice of denial is also published in the Register. The rule, if adopted, becomes effective not less than 30 days after the notice is published, unless delay would be impractical or contrary to public interest or in an emergency.

EXEMPTION PROCEDURES

A similar method to that used in requesting a proposed rule change should be used when requesting an exception to an existing rule. If for some valid reason a pilot, owner, FBO, etc., cannot meet the requirements of an FAA rule, either on his/her aircraft or for him/herself, the person may request an exemption (exception) from the rule.

The written request for the exemption should state the nature and extent of the relief requested. A description of each aircraft or the name of the person to be covered by the exemption must also be included. In addition, the statement should give reasons why granting the exemption would not adversely affect public safety or state the action required to provide the level of safety equal to that provided by the rule from which the exemption is requested.

The request, like the petition for a rule change, should be made in duplicate and mailed to the same address.

The Administrator may hold a hearing on the petition or may decide on its merits based on the material contained in the request. If the Administrator decides that a hearing is necessary to provide informed administrative action and assure adequate protection of private or public interests, the Administrator may hold an informal hearing. Any rule or order issued in a case in which a hearing is held need not be based solely on the evidence presented at the hearing. Prior to making a decision on a request, the Administrator is required to consult with the office of Chief Counsel for a legal opinion on the proposed action.

If the petition or request for an exception is denied, the petitioner may file a request for reconsideration with the Administrator within 30 days after the petitioner is notified of the denial of the request or exemption.

When a petition is granted, a person other than the initial petitioner may file a petition for reconsideration with the Administrator within 45 days after the request or grant of exemption.

If the exemption concerns a medical question, the petitioner may also request reconsideration from the Federal Air Surgeon.

Any petition for reconsideration must be based on the existence of one or more of the following:

- ☐ A finding of a material fact that is erroneous.
- ☐ A necessary legal conclusion that is without governing precedent or is a departure from or contrary to law, FAA rules, or precedent.
- ☐ An additional fact relevant to the decision that was not presented for exemption. In this case, the petition must state why the additional fact was not presented in the initial petition.

AIRWORTHINESS DIRECTIVES

The processing of proposed Airworthiness Directives is similar to the general rule making procedure noted above. The authority for issuing Airworthiness Directives is limited to the Director of Airworthiness, the Regional Directors for products under those regions, and the Chief Counsel.

FEDERAL AVIATION ADMINISTRATION PUBLICATIONS

Federal Aviation Administration publications are divided into two groups, one reflecting FAA's regulatory and technical functions, the other, non-regulatory and support functions. The regulatory and technical functions grouping includes Federal Aviation Regulations (FARs), Code of Federal Regulations Material, Type Certificates, parts manufacturer approvals, Airworthiness Directives, flight standard proms, air carrier utilization, airman's information materials, airman/aircraft information, Technical Standard Orders, FAA directives, Service Difficulty Reports, scientific and technical reports, agency progress reports, and the national airspace systems documents.

There are eleven categories of publications under the non-regulatory and support function aspect of the FAA. They deal with Advisory Circulars, aeromedical reports, aviation and career materials, agency approvals, flight safety materials, economic studies, historic monograms, booklets, pamphlets, brochures, planning and forecast projections, statistical reports, and the aviation safety magazine.

Federal Aviation Regulations (FARs)

FARs are issued by the FAA for implementation of its regulatory function. The FARs are the body of rules and regulations governing the qualifications, certifications, and operation of aircraft, pilots, instructors, etc. They are a rewrite of the former Civil Air Regulations. The FARs are continually being reviewed to meet changing needs. They carry the force of law and are binding on all aviation activities within their purview. Current FARs and changes to them are made available to the public through the Superintendent of Documents, U.S. Government Printing Office.

FARs previously organized in volumes are now sold by the Superintendent of Documents as individual parts. There are currently 45 such parts and 26 of the most frequently amended are sold on a subscription basis, the remaining 39 on a non-subscription, single-sale basis. Changes are sent automatically to those who have subscriptions. Changes to non-subscription items are required to be ordered separately when issued. The status of a Federal Aviation Regulation may be obtained by referring to Advisory Circular 00-44, Status of Federal Aviation Regulations. This Advisory Circular is free to the public and available at most FAA Regional Offices and centers.

Code of Federal Regulations (CFRs)

A portion of Title 14 of the Code of Federal Regulations deals with the

FAA. It includes a codification of the general and permanent rules published in the Federal Register by the FAA and brought up-to-date each year by the office that publishes the Federal Register.

Title 14 CFR as it pertains to the FAA is available in three of the five volumes of Title 14. The CFRs provide a summary of current rules and regulations published by the FAA, and are available at most major libraries.

Type Certification

FAA issues Type Certificates for new aircraft models, engines, and propellers when it determines that they meet the prescribed safety standards. When issuing a Type Certificate, FAA sets forth in the Type Certificate data sheet or specifications of those essential factors and other conditions which are necessary for the U.S. Airworthiness Certificate. The FAA also issues a Supplemental Type Certificate for major changes in the design of a Type Certified product when the change is not great enough to require the application of a new Type Certificate.

Type Certificate data sheets and specifications are published in a series of volumes, and are available from the Superintendent of Documents on a subscription basis. The Superintendent of Documents also sells a microfiche edition containing all current certificate data sheets and specifications. Supplemental Type Certificates are not available in data sheet format. However, they are listed in a summary of Supplemental Type Certificates issued when the holder indicates that parts, kits, data, and design rights are available to the public. The Superintendent of Documents sells a summary on a subscription basis with supplements issued each year.

Parts Manufacturer Approval (PMA)

The Parts Manufacturer Approval is a publication on a 24X microfilm format. It lists parts manufacturer approvals that have been issued under the requirement prescribed in part 21, subpart K of the Federal Aviation Regulations.

The FAA issues PMA approvals to an applicant for the production, modification, or replacement parts that may be installed on a Type Certificated product for which they are eligible. In order to seek a PMA, the applicant must allow the Administrator to make any inspection or tests necessary to determine compliance with the applicable Federal Aviation Regulation. Each holder of a PMA must establish and maintain a fabrication inspection system that ensures that each completed part conforms to its assigned data and is safe for installation on an applicable type aircraft. These approvals are of interest to mechanics, operators of repair stations, and others engaged in altering, inspecting, or maintaining aircraft who need to determine whether certain modifications or replacement of parts are approved for installation on that aircraft.

Airworthiness Directives (AD)

The FAA monitors products it has certified. In the case of aircraft, engines, propellers, or parts that have been certified but later found to be defective, the FAA issues Airworthiness Directives (AD), which require correction of the deficiencies. The ADs are a matter of record and issued to the public in two separate summaries or volumes. One is for small airplanes with the actual certified takeoff weight of 12,500 pounds or less; the other is for large aircraft or those aircraft with certified takeoff weight above 12,500 pounds. Each volume contains two separate books. Book One contains ADs issued prior to December 1970; Book Two contains those issued since that date. The Aeronautical Center at Oklahoma City has been designated as the FAA exclusive agent to sell the volumes to the public.

Paper copies of Book One, Volumes One and Two are sold without subscription as single-sell items. Because of the infrequency of changes to the older ADs contained in Book One, changes will only be incorporated by publishing new or revised editions. Paper copies of Book Two, Volumes One and Two are sold by subscription only. Subscription service includes the basic summary book and biweekly supplements for a two-year period.

A microfilm edition is sold by subscription only. One consolidated file of all four books is prepared annually. Subscription service includes the basic volumes and one year's supplemental information issued biweekly.

To obtain a subscription to the books, orders should be sent to the U.S. Department of Transportation, Federal Aviation Administration, Attention General Accounting Branch AAC-23, P.O. Box 25461, Oklahoma City, OK 73125, telephone (405) 686-4878.

Airman's Information Materials

There are five continuing publications on airman's information materials. The frequency of each depends in each case on the nature of the data. If the data is time-critical, then the material is issued more frequently—less frequently if the material is not time critical. Most of the publications are for sale by the Superintendent of Documents, U.S. Government Printing Office, on an annual subscription basis. Of the five publications, four deal with domestic and one with international operations. The domestic publications are the *Airman's Information Manual, Airport Facility Directory, Notices to Airmen,* and the *United States Aeronautical Information Publication.*

The *Airman's Information Manual* contains basic flight information and aircraft traffic control procedures. It is issued every 112 days. This publication contains the basic fundamentals required for safe flight in the U.S. National Airspace System. It includes chapters on navigation aids, airspace, air traffic control, flight safety, good operating procedures, and a pilot/comptroller glossary.

The *Airport Facility Directory* (A/FD) is published every 56 days by the National Ocean Service. The A/FD is a publication designed primarily as a pilot operational manual containing airports, seaplane bases, and heliports open to the public, communications data, navigational facilities, and certain special notices and procedures. The A/FD is available in seven volumes, each covering a specific geographical region of the continental United States, Puerto Rico, and the U.S. Virgin Islands. The bound volumes provide information on each airport, associated city and state runway characteristics, lighting, communications, and radio navaids.

The A/FD is offered on a subscription basis for one year, or it may be bought by single volumes. It should be ordered from NOAA, Distribution Branch, N/CG 33, National Ocean Service, Riverdale, Maryland 20737.

The third publication under the Airman's Information Materials is the *Notices to Airmen* (NOTAMs). This document is issued biweekly. The publication consists basically of current Notices to Airmen—information that is considered essential to the safety of flight and flight data center operations. Included in NOTAMs are amendments to instrument approach procedures and airspace restrictions. This document may be obtained on a subscription basis from the Superintendent of Documents, U.S. Government Printing Office.

The *United States Aeronautical Information Publication* (AIP) is a comprehensive aeronautical publication containing regulations and data required for safe aircraft operations in the National Airspace System. It is produced in accordance with recommended standards of the International Civil Aviation Organization. It is sold on a subscription basis; the subscription service includes the basic publication and changes, which are issued every 16 weeks.

There are two FAA international information materials under the Airman's Information Section. The first is the *International Flight Information Manual* (IFIM), which is published annually in April and amended in July, October, and January. This manual is published for use by private fliers, businessmen, and non-scheduled operators as a preflight and planning guide for flights outside the United States. It includes a directory of airports of entry, embassy information, pertinent entry regulations and restrictions, and passport, visa, and health requirements for each country.

The other FAA international material publication is the *International Notices to Airmen* (IN). This is issued biweekly; the publication is special to airmen service with emphasis on providing airmen with notices of significant navigational changes abroad.

The two international information publications may also be ordered from the National Ocean Service at Riverdale, Maryland, noted above.

Airmen/Aircraft Information

Information concerning currently listed airpersons and aircraft owners which previously appeared in the Civil Aircraft Registry is now available on microfiche with each FAA General Aviation District Office or Flight Standards District Office. The Civil Aircraft Registry is no longer published. In order to find out information regarding an individual item, simply call your nearest GADO or FSDO and provide them with the registration number or N-number of the airplane, or, if that is not known, give the airman's name and current address or the state in which he resides.

Microfiche FAA reports are for sale on airmen/aircraft information. To obtain information, contact ANACOMP, Inc., 4545 North Lincoln Blvd., Suite 275, Oklahoma City, OK 73105, telephone (405) 528-8977.

The reports available from ANACOMP, Inc. are the Airman Directory, U.S. Civil Aircraft Registry by N-number, alphabetical listing of aircraft registrants, state and county list of aircraft registrants, and aircraft manufacturer and models. These reports are also available on magnetic tape from Myriad Computer Systems, Inc., 7720 North Robinson, B-7, Oklahoma City, OK 73116, telephone (405) 842-4480.

Technical Standard Orders (TSO)

The Technical Standard Orders are issued by the FAA Administrator, setting forth in detail minimum performance standards for specific articles, materials, parts, appliances, etc., to be used on civil aircraft. A list of some TSOs, and Technical Standards Orders procedures, are incorporated in the FARs, part 21, Certification Procedures for Products and Parts.

For a list and order information about the remaining TSOs, request a free copy of Advisory Circular 20-110, "Index of Aviation Technical Standard Orders," from the Department of Transportation, Publication Section, M-494.3, Washington, D.C. 20590.

Interested persons may petition the FAA Administrator to revise or issue a new TSO by submitting a description of the revision sought or of the new article for which a TSO is requested. In the petition, you should include your name, address, a telephone contact number, and justification for the request.

The source for obtaining copies of specific TSOs or being placed on the mailing list to receive draft TSO proposals is: FAA, Office of Airworthiness, Aircraft Engineering Division, Technical Analysis Branch (AWS-120), 800 Independence Avenue S.W., Washington, D.C. 20591. In addition, notices of proposed TSOs are published in the Federal Register. Comments from the public are invited within 90 days of any publication.

FAA Directives

The FAA publishes and has available for sale through the Superintendent of Documents, Government Printing Office, a series of directives. The more popular directives are the *Flight Services Handbook, Data Communications Handbook, Air Traffic Control Handbook, Contractions Handbook, Location Identifiers,* and the *U.S. Standards for Terminal Instrument Procedures* (TERPS).

The *Flight Services Handbook* describes procedures and phraseology used by personnel providing flight assistance and communications service. The *Data Communications Handbook* is issued every 112 days, and it concerns U.S. Service weather schedules. This material was formerly contained in Part II of the *Flight Services Handbook.*

The *Air Traffic Control Handbook,* also published every 112 days, prescribes procedures and phraseology for use by the air traffic control personnel. It also defines their operational responsibilities, and discusses the quality of judgment that they are expected to demonstrate in discharging their responsibilities.

The *Contractions Handbook* is a basic manual containing approved word and phrase contractions used by the FAA and other agencies involved in air traffic communications, charting, and related aviation services.

The *Location Identifiers Handbook* is issued every 112 days. This handbook lists the location identifiers authorized by the Federal Aviation Administration, the Department of the Navy, and Transport Canada. It lists U.S. airspace fixes and procedure codes. The handbook also includes guidelines for requesting identifiers and procedures for making assignments. An identifier for an airport would be the three-letter call sign normally used. For example, Los Angeles International Airport's identifier is LAX.

The *U.S. Standard for Terminal Instrument Procedures* (TERPS) contains criteria which are to be used to formulate, review, approve, and publish procedures for instrument approach and departure of aircraft to and from civil and military airports. These criteria are for application at any location over which an appropriate U.S. agency exercises jurisdiction.

In addition to the above listed six headquarters publications, there are other directives available for sale to the public by FAA. You may obtain a detailed list by requesting from the Public Inquiry Staff in FAA Headquarters, a copy of "Washington Headquarters Directives Checklist." The prices of the directives are largely determined by the number of pages, which is normally six cents per page with a minimum charge of $1.00.

Service Difficulty Reports

The Aviation Standard National Field Office at Oklahoma City issues two types of Service Difficulty Reports. The first alerts recipients to reported air carrier service difficulties. The other alerts general aviation as to service difficulties.

Individuals or organizations who wish to be put on the mailing list for one or the other of these weekly publications may apply to the Aviation Standard National Field Office, Attention: AVN-120, P.O. Box 25082, Oklahoma City, OK 73125. Included in the application should be reasons why the individual wishes to be put on that list.

The Aviation National Field Office at Oklahoma City will also provide persons with an ADP printout of Service Difficulties for general aviation or air carrier aviation for a small fee. Requests for this service should be directed to the above listed Aviation Standards National Field Office at Oklahoma City.

The above service, together with computer printouts of accident and incident information, may also be obtained from commercial sources. The three most popular commercial sources are the Aircraft Owners and Pilots Association, Aircraft and Airman's Records Department, P.O. Box 19244, Southwest Station, Oklahoma City, OK 73144, telephone (800) 654-6700; AVDATA, P.O. Box 19053, Oklahoma City, OK 73144, telephone (405) 685-2881; and Capital Systems Group, Inc., 11301 Rockville Pike, Kensington, MD 20705, telephone (301) 881-9400.

Scientific and Technical Reports

The FAA makes available to the public through NTIS various scientific and technical reports. Included in this category are research and development (RD) reports. The FAA issues a quarterly press release listing the reports, which usually total several hundred each year, by date of issue, number of pages, and NTIS number. Also included in the release is the page ring price schedule. (Note: The first price given in any NTIS report is for the paper copy, and the second is for the microfiche copy.) Copies of current release can also be secured from FAA Headquarters, Department APA-300. Requests to be put on the mailing list for future releases should also be addressed to Department APA-300, FAA Headquarters, 800 Independence Avenue S.W., Washington, D.C. 20591.

Non-Regulatory and Support Functions

The FAA publishes 11 categories of publications considered non-regulatory and support functions. Probably the most important is Advisory Circulars and question books. The Advisory Circular checklist is published as necessary and is free to the public. FAA also sells question books which contain questions to use in preparation for particular certification or ratings in various aircraft categories. The books are designed to be used as a source of questions for official FAA written tests, and as for study guides for use by applicants. After taking an FAA test, the applicant will receive an airmen written test report, which indicates the test score and will also list the actual question numbers of each question answered incorrectly. The applicant may then refer to the question book to locate and identify these questions.

The current Advisory Flight Test Guides are also being replaced by a new series of publications that will be called Practical Test Standards.

The FAA is incorporating in the testing area the 13 Advisory Circular Flight Test Guides into six loose-leaf Practical Test Standards books. Each book will be divided into sections that will apply to a particular aircraft category and class. For example, the Private Pilot Practical Test Standards book will include:

- ☐ Section 1—Airplane Single Engine Land
- ☐ Section 2—Airplane Multi-Engine Land
- ☐ Section 3—Airplane Single Engine Sea
- ☐ Section 4—Airplane Multi-Engine Sea
- ☐ Section 5—Rotorcraft Helicopter
- ☐ Section 6—Rotorcraft Gyroplane
- ☐ Section 7—Glider
- ☐ Section 8—Lighter-than-Air, Airship
- ☐ Section 9—Lighter-than-Air, Free Balloon

The other five standards books are the Commercial Pilot, Airplane Transport Pilot, Type Rating, Instrument Rating, and Flight Instructor. Those books are divided into sections similar to that described for the Private Pilot.

The books present the practical test in outline format and objective terminology. Each task in a particular test contains the knowledge and skill requirements with appropriate tolerances to permit the pilot examiner to objectively evaluate the performance of pilot applicants. Instructors will be able to use the guides as an indication of the performance standards that will be required of their students.

The Government Printing Office sells publications on a subscription basis. In addition, some will be sold on a single item sale. Check with local Superintendent of Documents bookstore for current status of the advisory circular.

The FAA also carries approximately 400 free Advisory Circulars. These may be obtained from any FAA Public Affairs office or Flight Standards District Office. For advisory circulars, the prefix is AC. When requesting an Advisory Circular, be sure to cite the Advisory Circular number proceeded by the prefix AC. AC00-2 "Advisory Circular Checklist" is a list of the current top Advisory Circular choices available free of charge from the FAA.

Aeromedical Reports

Aeromedical Reports are published by the FAA, Office of Aviation Medicine (AAM). For the most part, these reports represent the work done at the agency's Civil Aeromedical Institute (CAMI), which is a staff section of the Aeronautical Center at Oklahoma City. They also include, however, reports prepared by headquarters and other regional medical personnel. Since 1961, the Office of Aviation Medicine has published approximately 600 Aeromedical Reports. These reports are available at NTIS and are listed in the AAM publication. In addition, they are available from the FAA Aeronautical Center, AAC-140, P.O. Box 25082, Oklahoma City, OK 73125.

Educational and Career Materials

The FAA provides certain publication for educators and students regarding aviation and aviation career guidance materials designed to enhance and enrich aviation study programs and/or to attract students to aviation careers. These may be obtained, free of charge, from the Consignment Branch, Superintendent of Documents, Washington, D.C. 20402. A list of these documents may also be obtained from that address.

Agency Approvals

The FAA issues listings of FAA-approved medical examiners, parachute riggers, engineering representatives, parts manufacturers, materials, parts and appliances, aviation maintenance technical schools, pilot school repair stations, and parachute lofts. The current listings include a directory of aviation medical examiners, FAA-designated mechanics examiner directory, designated engineering representatives, parts manufacturer approval, FAA inspection authorization directory, directory of FAA-certified aviation maintenance technician schools, list of certified pilot schools, and FAA-certificated maintenance agency directories.

Flight Safety Materials

The FAA publishes two types of flight safety materials—the VFR and IFR Exam-o-grams, published by the Examination Standard Branch, and the Flight Standard Safety pamphlets, published at FAA Headquarters as part of the FAA General Accident Prevention Program.

OTHER GOVERNMENT ORGANIZATIONS INVOLVED IN AVIATION

In addition to the FAA functions, there are other government agencies that have overlapping responsibility with the FAA regarding aviation safety (Fig. 3-1). The functions performed by the three major agencies—the Office of the Secretary of Transportation, the National Transportation Safety Board, and the National Ocean Service—are summarized as follows:

Office of the Secretary of Transportation (OST)

While the FAA is responsible for aircraft safety, one of the Office of the Secretary of Transportation's responsibilities is the economic regulation of certificated air carriers. Accordingly, OST deals with service problems encountered by airline passengers., These include such things as disputes over fares, lost or damaged luggage, poor service, discourteous treatment, delayed flights, and cancelled reservations. The OST has established an Office of Community and Consumer Affairs (OCCA) to take care of such matters. The OCCA encourages consumers first to contact the airline. If, however, they are unsatisfied, they may call an OCCA representative at (202) 755-2220 and that office will attempt to resolve the problem.

Federal Communications Commission
Gettysburg, PA 17326

Approved by OMB
3060-0040
Expires 3/31/89

APPLICATION FOR AIRCRAFT RADIO STATION LICENSE

- Read instructions above before completing application.
- Use typewriter or print clearly in ink.
- Sign and date application.
- Place First Class Postage on the reverse side of the card and mail.

1. FAA Registration or FCC Control Number. (If FAA Registration is not required for your aircraft, explain in item 8.) N

2. Is application for a fleet license? ☐ No ☐ Yes
If yes, give the number of aircraft in fleet, including planned expansion ....

3. Type of applicant (check one)
☐ I—Individual ☐ C—Corporation
☐ P—Partnership ☐ D—Individual with Business Name
☐ A—Association ☐ G—Governmental entity

4. Applicant/Licensee Name (See Instructions)

5. Mailing Address (Number and Street, P.O. Box or Route No., City, State, ZIP Code)

6. Frequencies Requested (check appropriate box(es) in 6A and/or 6B.)

6A. DO NOT CHECK BOTH BOXES
☐ A—Private Aircraft ☐ C—Air Carrier

6B. ADDITIONAL INFORMATION IS REQUIRED IF YOU CHECK HERE (See Instructions)
☐ T—Flight Test HF ☐ V—Flight Test VHF ☐ P—Portable ☐ O—Other (Specify)

7. Application is for:
☐ New Station ☐ Renewal
☐ Modification

8. Answer space for any required statements

9. READ CAREFULLY BEFORE SIGNING: 1. Applicant waives any claim to the use of any particular frequency regardless of prior use by license or otherwise. 2. Applicant will have unlimited access to the radio equipment and will control access to exclude unauthorized persons. 3. Neither applicant nor any member thereof is a foreign government or representative thereof. 4. Applicant certifies that all statements made in this application and attachments are true, complete, correct and made in good faith. 5. Applicant certifies that the signature is that of the individual, or partner, or officer or duly authorized employee of a corporation, or officer who is a member of an unincorporated association, or appropriate elected or appointed official on behalf of a governmental entity.

WILLFUL FALSE STATEMENTS MADE ON THIS FORM ARE PUNISHABLE BY FINE AND/OR IMPRISONMENT U.S. CODE TITLE 18. SECTION 1001

10. Signature

Date

FCC 404
June 1986

Fig. 3-1. Application for Aircraft Radio Station License. The FAA requires that each aircraft radio be licensed with the FCC. Note that in the application, the applicant states that the applicant will control access to the radio and exclude unauthorized persons from using the radio. Control of radio airways is one of the many functions that the FAA shares with other governmental agencies.

National Transportation Safety Board (NTSB)

The NTSB is discussed in detail in Chapter 1.

National Ocean Service (NOS)

This agency is a component of the National Oceanic and Atmospheric Administration (NOAA) of the Department of Commerce. It publishes and sells to the public aeronautical charts and maps used in air operations. The NOS issues a free 40-page brochure entitled "Catalog of Aeronautical Charts and Related Publications." This brochure lists in detail the aeronautical charts of domestic and foreign areas that is available for sale. The catalog includes a listing of all authorized aeronautical chart sales agencies. These sales agencies are usually private firms at airports who buy the charts from NOS at a discount and sell them at list price.

These charts may also be obtained from NOS, whose address is: National Ocean Service, Distribution Branch N/CG-33, 6501 Lafayette Avenue, Riverdale, MD 20737, telephone (301) 436-8194.

Chapter 4

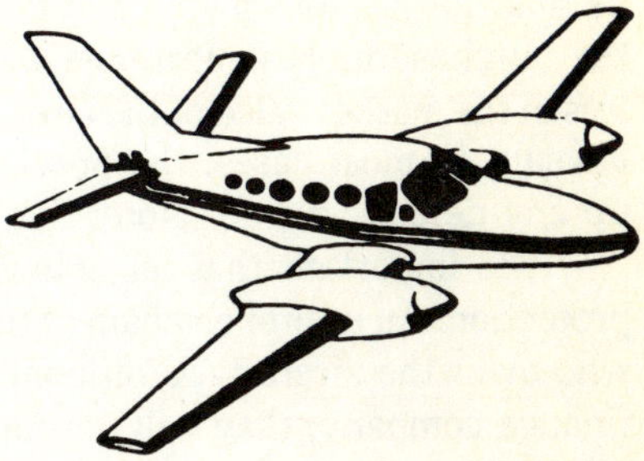

Aircraft Purchases and Registration

The purchase of an aircraft represents a substantial investment on the part of the new owner. Thus it is important that he receives a clear title to the aircraft. A *clear title* is one with no liens, chattel mortgages, or other unsatisfied claims on record against it. A clear title is considered a marketable title.

AIRCRAFT TITLE

The title of an airplane is similar to the deed on a home or on a parcel of land. All records concerning the ownership of your home and any mortgages and liens against it are recorded at the local county seat. In the case of airplanes, these records are maintained by the federal government. They are filed with the Aircraft Registration Branch of the FAA in Oklahoma City, Oklahoma. The aircraft records, like those on your home, are open for public inspection. Accordingly, if you wish to know who owns a certain aircraft and what liens are on it, this may be accomplished by a visit to the Aircraft Registration Branch. (In most cases, a professional title researcher can do this for you. See the discussion later in this chapter on title search companies.)

To ensure a clear title on the newly acquired airplane, there is no substitute for a title search prior to completing the contract of purchase. The search consists of checking the records at the Aircraft Registration Branch for any document that has been recorded against the aircraft in question. A list of the recorded documents makes up the aircraft's *document history*.

You would not consider purchasing a home from even the most reputable real estate dealer without a title search on the property. Therefore, the same precautions should be followed when purchasing a new or used aircraft. Many owners have suffered headaches from failing to take this precaution.

Any mortgage, lien, or other document on record against the interest of the aircraft owner is considered as a "cloud" on the title. This defect may only be that the previous owner had failed to record a release from the bank when the purchase money mortgage was paid off. However, even this defect can lessen the market value of the aircraft, since no one wants to purchase a possible lawsuit. In most cases, the previous owner is given an opportunity to clear up any defects in title. Note: See discussion below on escrow procedures.

It is important that an unbroken chain of title be established for your protection. An unbroken chain of title is one that indicates *without any questions* who owns the aircraft. Additionally, if your aircraft is financed by a bank or finance company, they will normally require the title search to protect their interests.

The aircraft registry is open to the public and anyone may conduct his own search by going to it in Oklahoma City. Since most individuals are not proficient in this and are not located in Oklahoma City, it is recommended that a title search company be used. There are a number of these companies that advertise in the aviation magazines. In selecting a title search company, the key item to look for is that the company is bonded.

A title search company located in Oklahoma City can search the title to the airplane in a matter of hours and will provide you with a telephone report on the status of the title, followed by a written confirmation by mail. If the title company overlooks a cloud on the title, in most cases the title company is liable for negligence. If the company is still in business, they can be sued. If the company is no longer in business or is bankrupt, then a claim may be filed against the title search company's bond.

When buying an aircraft, the recommended procedure is to include in the contract or purchase a guarantee that the title to the airplane is clear, that is, without any clouds on it. An escrow arrangement should be used. This is where a third person or company holds the purchase money and the title document until a clear title is established. The third party should be one whom both they buyer and seller trust. This method is used in the purchase of almost all real estate. Most banks or title companies will handle this for you for a reasonable fee. Needless to say, the escrow agent must be selected carefully.

The document history that you should receive as the result of the title search includes:

- ☐ Present registered aircraft owner.
- ☐ All previous registered owners.
- ☐ Liens of record—dates, amounts, and lien holders.
- ☐ Lien releases—dates and amounts.
- ☐ Aircraft periodic status.
- ☐ Total airframe hours at last periodic inspection.

☐ Total engine hours at last periodic inspection.
☐ Detail equipment listing.
☐ Case history of any legal actions concerning the aircraft.
☐ Aircraft damage and repair history.
☐ Aircraft serial identification.
☐ Aircraft model identification.
☐ Aircraft airworthiness status.
☐ Aircraft modifications and AD compliance status.

Here is the general fee schedule used by one title company in 1986:

Aircraft title search (Older aircraft extra)	$35.00
Title search update	25.00
Engine search	30.00
Pilot check	30.00
Chain of title (May vary depending on size of chain)	30.00
Present registered owner information	15.00
Filing documents (plus FAA fee)	20.00
Photocopies (plus FAA fee)	10.00
Certified copy of lien document for filing (plus FAA fee)	5.00
Duplicate certificate	10.00
N number reservation (plus FAA fee)	50.00
Request for special searching time	10.00 per hour

Here are the FAA fees:

Photocopies (each side)	$ .50
Lien documents	5.00
Disclaimers	5.00
Application for registration	5.00
Lease	5.00
Lien on engine	5.00
Federal storage fee	2.00
Certified copies	3.00
Duplicate certificates	2.00
Special N number reservation	10.00

CONTESTED OWNERSHIP OF AIRCRAFT

Controversies over the ownership of airplanes are not determined by the FAA, but are settled by local courts in accordance with local laws. Thus, in any case where the ownership is contested and has been determined by a court order, a copy of the court order should be filed with the FAA. The certificate of registration issued by the FAA is to the person who appears to be the owner of the airplane.

The FAA is without authority to refuse recordation and registration of documents submitted, as long as the documents appear to be eligible on their face. Thus, if a bill of sale *looks* valid and is from the person who is *on record* as the apparent owner of the airplane, the FAA is required to register it.

As mentioned earlier, a title search will reveal any claims of ownership against the airplane in question. Thus, the buyer will be able to determine if the title is in dispute before he/she completes the purchase. Generally, the buyer is safe when he/she purchases an airplane with no adverse claims against the ownership. Exceptions to this apparent ownership most often occur when there is a forged title in the chain of ownership. There is some protection against this, since most transfers of title must be signed before a notary. If in doubt, check with previous owners.

Any owner of an aircraft that has an adverse claim filed against it may take action in a local court to have the title cleared. The methods and procedures for doing this vary with each state. A local attorney should be able to provide guidance in this matter. The usual method is to file a petition in the appropriate court requesting that ownership of the airplane in question be determined. The court then issues a writ to each party claiming an interest in the airplane and is under the jurisdiction of the court to come into court and substantiate his or her claim.

The failure of a party (person involved) to make an appearance or to submit an answer to the writ will defeat his/her claim if the party is within the jurisdiction of the court. In some cases, if the parties live in different states, the case may be tried in federal court in order to obtain jurisdiction over citizens of different states. If the case cannot be tried in federal court and involves people with adverse claims in more than one state, the issue may need to be ligated in several state courts.

A court will normally have jurisdiction over a party if the party can be personally served with a writ or petition of the court. In most cases, the petition or writ may be served only in the state in which the state court is located. In the case of federal cases, a federal court's writ may be served anywhere in the United States.

As noted earlier, any court order deciding the status of claims on an airplane should be filed with the aircraft registry in Oklahoma City.

AIRCRAFT OWNER RESPONSIBILITIES

The aircraft owner has certain responsibilities placed on him/her by the FARs and federal and state statutes similar to those placed on owners of automobiles. An automobile owner is required to register his/her car and obtain license plates for it. An owner of an airplane has the following responsibilities:

- ☐ Having a current Airworthiness Certificate appropriately displayed in the airplane.
- ☐ Maintaining the aircraft in an airworthy condition.
- ☐ Assuring that maintenance is properly recorded.
- ☐ Keeping up with current regulations concerning the operation and maintenance of the airplane.
- ☐ Notifying the FAA Aircraft Registry immediately of any change of permanent mailing address or of the sale or dismantling of the aircraft.
- ☐ Notifying the FAA Aircraft Registry immediately of major modifications to the airplane to include engine or propeller changes.
- ☐ Complying with state regulations and statutes regarding the licensing and operation of the aircraft.

AIRCRAFT FINANCING

The majority of potential aircraft owners are not in a position to pay cash for their airplanes, and in these cases the method of financing is important. In the area of airplane financing, it pays to shop around.

The aircraft dealer, if one is involved, is usually in a position to direct you to a reputable commercial finance company. The dealer, however, is interested not in getting the *best* deal for the buyer, but in finding a company that will finance the sale. The potential owner should shop around to find a bank or other institution that best serves his/her interests. It appears that the same approach that a potential buyer uses to find the most favorable auto loan would apply to airplane buyers. Credit unions have proved to be good places to start loan shopping.

Interest rates of various financial institutions are misleading, as the interest may be stated as either simple interest or add-on interest or may require a discounted loan. The best method of figuring the cost of a loan is to compute the total time price. Many institutions charge a service fee for making the loan. Consider this fee as a part of the actual cost of the loan.

Other items that are normally included in the loan costs are recording, title search, registration fees, and credit life insurance. The first three fees are necessary and should be included, but credit life insurance is not normally recommended since the premium rates for credit life is usually higher than the normal life insurance.

TRUTH IN LEASING CLAUSE

FAR 91.54 requires that parties to a lease or conditional sale involving a United States-registered large civil aircraft and entered into after January

2, 1973, shall execute a written lease or contract and include therein a written "truth in leasing" clause. For the exact wording of the clause, see FAR 91.54.

LEASE-BACK ARRANGEMENTS

Many aircraft owners have used lease-back agreements to help pay the monthly payments on the airplane loan. Under this method, the owner purchases a new aircraft and then leases it back to the dealer, who usually operates a flying school. When the aircraft is not being used, the owner may fly it.

There are several drawbacks to this type of arrangement that should be considered by the potential aircraft owner before entering into one. First, the aircraft is flown many more hours than a normal pilot would fly his/her own airplane. In addition, the care of the airplane by renter pilots is in many cases less protective than by the owner. These two factors will increase the maintenance costs of owning an airplane.

Another disadvantage of the arrangement is that during the first two years, when the aircraft is new, the demand to fly it is greater. As the airplane gets older, however, the demand will be less and thus the income less. However, the monthly installment payments on the loan continue. An additional disadvantage is that many times the aircraft is not available when the owner wants it.

The Tax Reform Act has eliminated the investment tax credit that was a substantial benefit to owners using lease-back arrangements. In many cases, the investment tax credit paid for 10 percent of the cost of the airplane. While an owner using the lease-back may still depreciate the airplane and receive some tax benefits from this, the Tax Reform Act also reduces the benefit of this deduction by lowering the tax rates and placing restrictions on passive income losses.

AIRCRAFT WARRANTIES

Aircraft warranties are either expressed or implied. An *expressed warranty* is one made to induce the buyer to purchase the aircraft. It may be made either orally or in writing. An *implied warranty* is one that the courts will imply as a necessary part of the contract without any mention of it by either of the parties involved. In many cases, a warranty may be both implied by law and expressed by the agreement of the parties.

The implied warranties in the purchase of an aircraft include the following:

- ☐ That the seller has a right to sell the aircraft in question.
- ☐ That the seller has the authority to give the buyer a legal title to the aircraft, or will have it at the time the title is due to change.
- ☐ That the aircraft is free from all adverse claims by other people, unless the buyer is advised of the claims.

There is no implied warranty when the seller informs the buyer that the title is defective or that he/she does not have the power to transfer a clear title. A similar rule applies if the buyer is aware of the defects prior to closing the sale. This latter rule applies only to those defects that the buyer is aware of.

On the breach of an implied warranty, the buyer may sue the seller for damages, or, if the sale is not completed, he/she may rescind the contract. In the normal case, any breaches of implied warranties of title will be discovered during the title search. If the purchase money is being held in escrow, the buyer would normally have a right to return of the purchase money. Failure of the escrow agent to return the money makes the agent potentially liable for the amount of money in question.

Unless the airplane is sold "as is" there is normally a general warranty of fitness. This warranty varies in each state, but normally means that it is warranted to be fit for the general purpose of flying unless the buyer is otherwise notified.

Express warranties on new airplanes are contained in warranty policies issued by the airplane manufacturers, similar to those issued for new automobiles. These policies are contractual in nature, in that the extent and limits of the warranty are contained in the policy. In addition, any requirements that the owner must comply with are contained in the policy (contract). For example, the policy may state that the warranty is void if the engine oil is not changed at certain intervals.

Used airplanes are subject to the above-noted implied warranties of title and, normally, fitness for the general purpose of flying. This latter warranty does not imply that the airplane is in perfect condition, only that there are no known major defects to the airplane and that no unauthorized maintenance has been performed on the plane.

Other types of warranties that may be expressed are that the aircraft has not been involved in an accident, that the fabric is "in the green," etc. However, warranties should be distinguished from statements of opinion. A warranty or statement of fact may make the seller liable for any false statements, whereas an erroneous opinion does not. A seller's statement as to the value of an airplane is only an opinion, whereas the statement that the seller has recently been offered $15,000 for the airplane is a statement of fact and thus if false may make the seller liable. In many cases, a warranty is considered as a guarantee.

When an expressed warranty has been breached, the buyer has a claim for damages against the seller, the same as when an implied one is breached. Most implied warranties, however, are not discovered until after the sale is completed. If the breach is substantial, the buyer may return the airplane for a refund of the purchase price plus other expenses incurred, or the buyer may retain the airplane and sue for damages. In cases where the breach by the seller was not deliberate, in many cases the seller must be given an opportunity to correct the problem first.

The buyer and seller may agree that the aircraft is to be sold without any warranties. This is an "as is" sale and the warranties of title still apply unless the seller specifically points out the lack of warranty of title. The seller may sell any claim that he/she has in the aircraft where the title is in dispute, provided that the buyer is aware of the facts.

PASSAGE OF TITLE

Title to the aircraft (ownership) passes to the buyer when the parties intend it to. Where the parties have not expressly stated their intention, it is determined by law as follows:

- ☐ When there is an unconditional contract of purchase, title passes at the time the contract is signed, even though payment and delivery may be at a later date.
- ☐ Where the contract is to sell an aircraft not yet manufactured, title passes when such aircraft is designated for the particular contract by the seller with the consent of the buyer.
- ☐ When the contract requires the seller to deliver the aircraft to a particular place, title passes when delivery is completed unless it has already passed under the above two situations.
- ☐ In a conditional sales contract, ownership does not pass until the terms of the contract are completed. In most cases, this is when the final payment of the purchase price is made.

The problem of when the title passes is important if an accident or damage to the aircraft occurs. In most states, the burden of loss will fall upon the owner. Therefore, if during the transition period the aircraft is totally destroyed, the buyer may be required to pay the purchase price for it. Thus, during this time it is important that the parties agree on the exact time that ownership will change. This will allow for each person to provide insurance to cover his/her period of ownership.

CONDITIONAL SALES CONTRACTS

When an airplane is purchased with borrowed money, the lender (one who loans the money) usually takes a chattel mortgage (personal property mortgage) on the aircraft to insure his/her investment. Therefore, the lender can better afford to lend the money, as it will be secured by the mortgage much like the chattel mortgage on a car. In some states, the mortgage is known as a *title lien.*

Chattel mortgage is a conditional sale, with the title to the aircraft belonging to the holder of the note (mortgage) until the terms of the mortgage are fulfilled (purchase money is paid).

Chattel mortgages derive their name from the early English practice of allowing only mortgages on land and cattle. Later, as the need for mortgages expanded, rather than change the mortgage restrictions, the common law defined the subject of all mortgages not on land as mortgages on "chattel."

If for any reason the loan is not paid when due, the lender may take legal steps to gain possession of the airplane and sell it according to the terms of the mortgage and applicable state statutes. If the aircraft is taken and sold pursuant to the mortgage, the proceeds are first applied to the costs of the sale, then the amount due on the loan. If any excess is left (rarely), the lender is obligated to return the surplus to the defaulting party. The steps required to be taken by the lender to foreclose on the mortgage or lien are governed by state law and are similar to those required in foreclosing on an automobile.

If the parties have a default clause in the original sale contract that requires certain steps be taken before the lender may foreclose, these steps must be followed or the lender may be sued for wrongful taking of the aircraft. In addition, in most states there are required statutory steps that must be taken prior to repossessing any items of property. Accordingly, advice of a local attorney is a necessity. To ensure that both the lender and the buyer are protected, a detailed default clause should be included in the original contract.

In some cases, the conditional sales contract may be defaulted by failure to take proper care of the airplane, by selling the aircraft without written permission of the lender, or by other actions contrary to the interests of the lender.

The Federal Aviation Act of 1958, as amended, provides that the states may regulate the method and form of aircraft mortgages, providing the regulations do not place an undue burden on interstate commerce. However, the recording provisions of the Federal Aircraft Registration Act concerning the recording of the contracts must be strictly followed to protect the lender. This will be discussed in detail later in this chapter.

The sample contract below is one suggested by the FAA and meets its requirements for recording. However, any provisions required by the appropriate state statute should be included.

Sample Conditional Sale Contract

(Note: Check local statutes for specific requirements.)

This contract of Conditional Sale is made this 1st day of May 19XX, by and between Joe Brown whose address is 155 South Street, New York, New York, hereafter referred to as the Seller, and Bill Smith whose address is 215 North Street, Houston, Texas, hereafter referred to as the Purchaser.

Witnesseth: That the Seller hereby grants, bargains, and sells to the Purchaser, his or her heirs, administrators, successors and assigns, and the Purchaser hereby purchases, subject to the terms and conditions herein set forth, the following described aircraft:

Aircraft make and model: Cessna 172
FAA registration number: N8191L

Manufacturer's serial number: 7453904
Engine serial number: 67593840

Together with all equipment and accessories attached thereto or used in connection therewith including the following: (list all major equipment including radios here) all of which are included in the term aircraft as used herein, for the sum of twenty-five thousand dollars ($25,000), of which $1,000.00 is payable upon the signing of this agreement, receipt thereof is hereby acknowledged by the Seller.

The purchaser hereby acknowledges delivery and acceptance of the aforesaid aircraft upon the following terms and conditions:

First: The payment of all indebtedness evidenced by and according to the terms of the promissory note, hereinbelow described, and any renewals and extensions thereof:

Note-bearing date of May 1, 19XX, executed by the purchaser and payable to the order of the First National Bank of Somerville, Maryland, in the aggregate of $24,000 with interest thereon at the rate of ten percent per annum, from the date note signed, payable in __________ monthly payments of __________ each on the 5th day of each successive month beginning with the 5th of June 19XX. The last payment of __________ is due on the 5th of June 19YY.

Second: The prompt and faithful discharge and performance of each agreement set forth herein in connection with the indebtedness to secure which this instrument is executed, and the repayment of any sums expended or advanced by the Seller for the maintenance or preservation of the aircraft sold under this contract or in enforcing his/her rights hereunder.

The Seller hereby declares and warrants to the said Purchaser that he/she is the sole owner of the legal title to the said aircraft, and that the said aircraft is free and clear of all liens, encumbrances, and adverse claims whatsoever.

Title to the said aircraft shall not pass to the Purchaser but shall remain in the Seller until such time as all sums due on the said aircraft are paid, and all other conditions fully performed. When all payments have been made and all conditions performed, the Seller agrees that absolute title shall pass to the purchaser.

Time is of the essence in this contract. It is hereby agreed that upon default in any terms of this contract, or if for any reason the seller should deem himself/herself insecure, then the whole principal sum then remaining unpaid, with accrued interest, shall immediately become due and payable at the option of the Seller.

In the event of default, the Seller may proceed to take possession of the said aircraft in the manner prescribed by law, and he/she is hereby empowered so to do, and with or without legal process enter upon the premises and take possession of the said aircraft; remove and sell or otherwise dispose of the said aircraft at public or private sale, and retain from the proceeds of such sale all costs and charges incurred by him/her in taking or sale of aircraft, including reasonable attorney's fees incurred and all sums due Seller under this contract. Any surplus of the proceeds shall be paid to the Purchaser, or whoever may be lawfully entitled to receive the same. If a deficiency results after resale, the buyer agrees to pay such deficiency forthwith.

(Acknowledgments according to local statutes.)

Joc Brown (Sellcr)

Bill Smith (Purchaser)

Recording Conditional Sales Contract

An unrecorded chattel mortgage will not defeat the rights of a later purchaser who had no knowledge of the existence of the mortgage. However, any mortgage that is recorded at the Aircraft Registry is presumed to be known to all prospective buyers. Unlike the title to an automobile, where ownership is reflected on the face of the title, in the case of aircraft, ownership is reflected by the documents on file with the FAA.

While the documents recorded are not necessarily valid, they are notice of any claims of ownership against the aircraft in question.

The importance of documents recorded is illustrated by a recent case in the federal courts. The court stated that the provisions of the Federal Aviation Registration Act protects persons who have purchased on faith of the documents on file at the FAA Air Registry. In this case, the buyer had conducted a records check on the aircraft. The seller had, however, placed an earlier mortgage on the aircraft to a third person. The earlier mortgage was recorded with the state, but not at the Air Registry. The court held that the earlier mortgage was invalid as to defeat the rights of the buyer and that he received a clear title unless it could be proved that the buyer was aware of the existence of the first mortgage.

In a similar case, the holder of the unrecorded mortgage actually had possession of the aircraft, yet the courts refused to give any effect to the unrecorded mortgage. The court stated that while possession may have raised the suspicion of some claim on the part of the possessor, the Recording Act required that to defeat the interest of the new buyer, actual knowledge of the unrecorded mortgage is required.

In recording any conditional sales contract or lien, ensure that the mortgage specifically describes the engines, as they are a major portion of the purchase price. One lender failed to accomplish this and he was unable to prove that the chattel mortgage covered the engines in the airplane after the engines had been removed. In this case, prior to defaulting on the contract, the buyer dismantled the engines and sold them.

One exception to the recording requirement is when the new owner received the aircraft as a gift or pays an unusually low price for the airplane. In this situation, he or she is not an innocent purchaser for value as he/she should have known that something was wrong. Accordingly, the new owner (who takes by way of gift or unusually low price) takes subject to the earlier unrecorded lien. This exception is based on the concept that the recording act is designed to protect innocent purchasers for value and not persons who received the aircraft under other conditions.

Release of Conditional Sales Contract

When the buyer has fulfilled the requirement of the conditional sales contract, title to the aircraft passes to him/her. To ensure that the owner has a clear title, it is necessary to record a release of all interest in the aircraft by the holder of the lien. Note: The buyer has a right to the release when the conditions are complied with and failure to issue one by the Seller is a violation of the contract. Listed below is a sample release. Check with local statutes to determine the specific requirements in your state.

Sample Release

The undersigned person is the true and lawful holder of the note or other evidence of indebtedness secured by the described contract of conditional sale on aircraft, FAA registration number N9181L dated the 1st day of May 19XX and executed by Joe Brown, conditional seller, and Bill Smith, conditional purchaser and assigned to the Aircraft Finance Company, St. Louis, Missouri.

This contract was recorded by the Federal Aviation Administration on May 5, 1986, and was assigned document number 34567234.

The undersigned is also the holder of the legal title to aircraft described as follows: Cessna 172, serial number 7453904, engine serial number 67593840, and FAA registration number N9181L.

For and in consideration of the payment in full of the indebtedness due under the above described contract of conditional sale, the undersigned hereby does on the 5th day of October 19XX, sell, grant, transfer, and deliver all of his right, title, and interest in the above described aircraft unto Bill Smith whose address is 215 North Street, Houston, Texas, and to any of his successors, heirs and assigns, to have and to hold the said aircraft forever.

In testimony whereof, I, Jerry Brown, President of the Aircraft Finance Company and on behalf of the Aircraft Finance Company, have set my hand and seal this 5th day of October, 19XX.

(Acknowledgement.)

/s/ Jerry Brown
President
Aircraft Finance Company

LIENS

A *mechanic's lien* is similar to a chattel mortgage except that it is usually temporary in nature. For example, when you have repair work performed on your aircraft by the local dealer, the dealer has a mechanic's lien on the aircraft for the value of the work and parts. Accordingly, the dealer may retain the aircraft until the bill is paid. The dealer may not, however, retain the aircraft for bills other than the current bill, unless he/she gets a court order to attach the aircraft.

Normally, a mechanic's lien does not have to be recorded. Yet the holder must retain possession and may not sell the aircraft.

A *creditor's lien* is one gained by a court order for a debt owed by the aircraft owner to the person seeking to have it attached. In this situation, the court order must normally be recorded, but there is no requirement that the creditor gain possession of the airplane. In addition, the lien may be the subject of debts that are not in any way related to the airplane. In most states, the court may order that the aircraft be sold to pay the creditor's lien.

The validity of liens on aircraft are governed by state law rather than federal law, but they are subject to federal regulations on recording.

AIRCRAFT REGISTRATION

After the purchase of an aircraft, the new owner must apply for a Certificate of Registration before he/she can fly the aircraft. For an aircraft to be eligible for registration, it must be owned by a U.S. resident and not be registered under the laws of another country.

The application for registration should be on the AC form 8050-1 (Application for Aircraft Registration). This form consists of three parts: an original (white) and two duplicate copies (green and pink). Instructions for completing and submitting this form are attached to the top of the form (Fig. 4-1).

The temporary (pink copy) should be retained in the aircraft until the permanent Certificate of Registration is received from the FAA. The temporary certificate is valid for a period of 90 days unless time is extended by the FAA.

With the application for registration, the proper fee must be included (note fees listed earlier), along with a bill of sale or other evidence of ownership.

FORM APPROVED
OMB NO. 2120-0029
EXP. DATE 10/31/84

UNITED STATES OF AMERICA DEPARTMENT OF TRANSPORTATION
FEDERAL AVIATION ADMINISTRATION-MIKE MONRONEY AERONAUTICAL CENTER
AIRCRAFT REGISTRATION APPLICATION

CERT. ISSUE DATE

UNITED STATES REGISTRATION NUMBER **N**

AIRCRAFT MANUFACTURER & MODEL

AIRCRAFT SERIAL No.

FOR FAA USE ONLY

TYPE OF REGISTRATION (Check one box)

☐ 1 Individual ☐ 2 Partnership ☐ 3 Corporation ☐ 4 Co-owner ☐ 5 Gov't ☐ 8 Foreign owned Corporation

NAME OF APPLICANT (Person(s) shown on evidence of ownership. If individual, give last name, first name, and middle initial.)

TELEPHONE NUMBER: ( ) –

ADDRESS (Permanent mailing address for first applicant listed.)

Number and street: ______

Rural Route: P.O. Box

CITY	STATE	ZIP CODE

☐ **CHECK HERE IF YOU ARE ONLY REPORTING A CHANGE OF ADDRESS**

ATTENTION! Read the following statement before signing this application.

A false or dishonest answer to any question in this application may be grounds for punishment by fine and / or imprisonment (U.S. Code, Title 18, Sec. 1001).

CERTIFICATION

I/WE CERTIFY

(1) That the above aircraft is owned by the undersigned applicant, who is a citizen (including corporations) of the United States.

(For voting trust, give name of trustee: ______) or

CHECK ONE AS APPROPRIATE.

a. ☐ A resident alien, with alien registration (Form 1-151 or Form 1-551) No. ______

b. ☐ A foreign-owned corporation organized and doing business under the laws of (state or possession) ______, and said aircraft is based and primarily used in the United States. Records of flight hours are available for inspection at ______

(2) That the aircraft is not registered under the laws of any foreign country; and
(3) That legal evidence of ownership is attached or has been filed with the Federal Aviation Administration.

NOTE: If executed for co-ownership all applicants must sign. Use reverse side if necessary.

TYPE OR PRINT NAME BELOW SIGNATURE

EACH PART OF THIS APPLICATION MUST BE SIGNED IN INK.	SIGNATURE	TITLE	DATE
	SIGNATURE	TITLE	DATE
	SIGNATURE	TITLE	DATE

NOTE. Pending receipt of the Certificate of Aircraft Registration, the aircraft may be operated for a period not in excess of 90 days, during which time the PINK copy of this application must be carried in the aircraft.

AC FORM 8050-1 (1-83) (0052-00-628-9005)

Fig. 4-1. Aircraft Registration Form 8050-1. This form is used in registration of aircraft when a change of ownership occurs. When this form is submitted, evidence of sale from the last registered owner should also be included. Note: This form may also be used to report changes of address for the registered owner.

Normally, the standard AC form 8050-2 (Aircraft Bill of Sale) is used as evidence of ownership (Fig. 4-2). Many aircraft dealers, however, prefer to use their own forms, and this is permissible.

Since one signed copy of the bill of sale must be submitted to the FAA with registration application, the new buyer needs to receive two signed copies. The buyer should retain one signed copy for the aircraft records and to establish evidence of ownership.

In many states, the bill of sale does not need to be signed before a notary public. However, since the cost of having it notarized is small, the acknowledgement is strongly recommended. The rule to follow is to be safe rather than sorry.

If for any reason the new owner can not submit a bill of sale with the application for registration, this must be explained when submitting the application for registration. The FAR (47.33) provides that the FAA may accept other evidence of ownership if the owner cannot for good cause provide a bill of sale. This other evidence may be an affidavit (sworn statement) stating why the bill of sale cannot be submitted, accompanied by whatever further evidence is available to prove the transaction.

Both the application for registration and the bill of sale must be signed in ink. The most common reason for rejection of these documents for registration by the FAA is because of improper signatures or failure to sign in ink. An improper signature is one where the signature of the buyer or seller is different from the typed name of the seller or buyer elsewhere on the form. For example, signing your name by the first two initials only where the first name is spelled out elsewhere on the form is considered as an improper signature.

The buyer is responsible for submitting the necessary applications. The seller is also responsible for notifying the FAA of the sale by completing the reverse side of the old Certificate of Registration and mailing it to the Aircraft Registry.

The effective date of registration is the date and time that the application is received and date/time stamped by the Registration Branch. In the event that more than one application is received on the same aircraft, the FAA accepts the documents bearing the earliest time and date stamp. Therefore, it is important that these documents be filed without delay.

Federal aviation rules require that an aircraft owner report any change in permanent mailing address within 30 days, at which time a revised Certificate of Aircraft Registration will be issued to the owner without cost.

A Certificate of Aircraft Registration will expire when:

- ☐ The aircraft is registered in a foreign country.
- ☐ On written request of the registered owner.
- ☐ The aircraft is destroyed or scrapped.
- ☐ Ownership of the aircraft is transferred.

FORM APPROVED
OMB No 2120-0029
EXP. DATE 10/31/84

UNITED STATES OF AMERICA
DEPARTMENT OF TRANSPORTATION FEDERAL AVIATION ADMINISTRATION

AIRCRAFT BILL OF SALE

FOR AND IN CONSIDERATION OF $ THE UNDERSIGNED OWNER(S) OF THE FULL LEGAL AND BENEFICIAL TITLE OF THE AIRCRAFT DESCRIBED AS FOLLOWS:

UNITED STATES
REGISTRATION NUMBER **N**

AIRCRAFT MANUFACTURER & MODEL

AIRCRAFT SERIAL No.

DOES THIS DAY OF 19
HEREBY SELL, GRANT, TRANSFER AND DELIVER ALL RIGHTS, TITLE, AND INTERESTS IN AND TO SUCH AIRCRAFT UNTO:

Do Not Write In This Block
FOR FAA USE ONLY

PURCHASER

NAME AND ADDRESS
(IF INDIVIDUAL(S), GIVE LAST NAME, FIRST NAME, AND MIDDLE INITIAL.)

DEALER CERTIFICATE NUMBER

AND TO EXECUTORS, ADMINISTRATORS, AND ASSIGNS TO HAVE AND TO HOLD SINGULARLY THE SAID AIRCRAFT FOREVER, AND WARRANTS THE TITLE THEREOF.

IN TESTIMONY WHEREOF HAVE SET HAND AND SEAL THIS DAY OF 19

SELLER

NAME (S) OF SELLER (TYPED OR PRINTED)	SIGNATURE (S) (IN INK) (IF EXECUTED FOR CO-OWNERSHIP, ALL MUST SIGN.)	TITLE (TYPED OR PRINTED)

ACKNOWLEDGMENT (NOT REQUIRED FOR PURPOSES OF FAA RECORDING: HOWEVER, MAY BE REQUIRED BY LOCAL LAW FOR VALIDITY OF THE INSTRUMENT.)

ORIGINAL: TO FAA

AC FORM 8050-2 (9-82) (0052-00-629-0002)

Fig. 4-2. Aircraft Bill of Sale above is the standard "bill of sale" form used by the FAA to establish evidence of sale. Note: Other forms may be used as long as they contain the required information; however, by using this form, the buyer is assured that it will be accepted by the FAA if properly completed. This form may be obtained from the FAA by requesting AC Form 8050-2.

- ☐ The aircraft owner loses his/her U.S. residency.
- ☐ On death of the registered owner.

CERTIFICATE OF AIRWORTHINESS

The Certificate of Airworthiness, unlike the Certificate of Registration, remains with the aircraft when ownership is transferred. This certificate remains in effect as long as the aircraft receives the proper maintenance and inspections and is operated within its specified limitations.

AIRCRAFT RECORDS

With the purchase of an aircraft, the new owner should receive the following documents:

- ☐ Bill of sale.
- ☐ Airworthiness Certificate.
- ☐ All logbooks, aircraft, and engine records.
- ☐ Equipment list.
- ☐ Maintenance manual, service letters, and bulletins.
- ☐ Weight and balance data.
- ☐ Airplane Flight Manual or operating limitations.

FALSIFICATION OF RECORDS

As per the FARs, it is unlawful for any person to:

- ☐ Make or cause to be made any fraudulent or intentionally false entry in any record or report that is required to be made, kept, or used to show compliance with any maintenance regulation.
- ☐ Make or cause to be made any reproduction, for fraudulent purpose, of any record or report required to be under Part 43, FARs.
- ☐ Make or cause to be made any alteration, for fraudulent purpose, any record or report required to made under Part 43, FARs.

Any of the above acts may be used as the basis for suspending or revoking the applicable airman, operator, or production certificate. In addition, it is a violation of federal law and thus subject to criminal penalties.

N-NUMBER

The N-number is the FAA registration number assigned to the aircraft. The N means that the aircraft is of U.S. registry. Normally, the number goes with the aircraft when it is sold. However, if the seller and buyer agree, the seller may retain and reserve the number. To do this, an application with appropriate fees must be forwarded to the Aircraft Registry. A new number will then be assigned the aircraft.

The N-number may be reserved for up to one year with a right of renewal. Once it is assigned to a new aircraft, then it continues to remain with that airplane until reassigned.

In most cases, the N-number must:

- ☐ Be painted on the aircraft or otherwise permanently affixed to the airplane.
- ☐ Have no ornamentation.
- ☐ Contrast in color with the background.
- ☐ Be legible.
- ☐ Be preceded by the Roman capital letter N.
- ☐ Be displayed horizontally on both sides of the fuselage.
- ☐ Be at least 12 inches high.

There are exceptions to the above requirements. The most usual one is the case of small aircraft at least 30 years of age or Experimental aircraft. For a full listing of the exceptions, see FARs 45.21 and 45.23.

Chapter 5

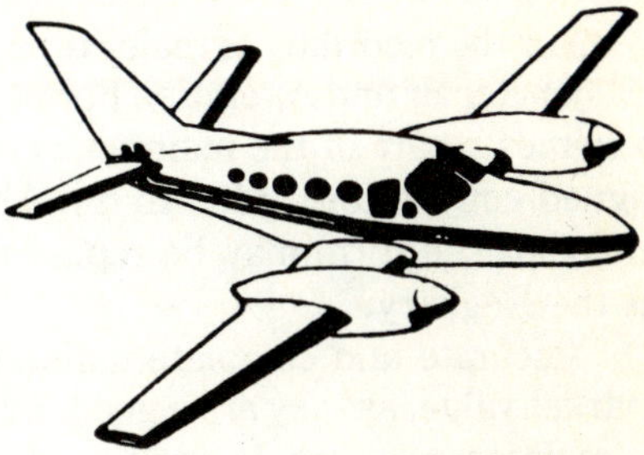

Aircraft Maintenance Rules

In this chapter, FAA rules pertaining to aircraft maintenance are discussed. FAR 43 contains the detail rules regarding maintenance, preventive maintenance, rebuilding, and alteration of aircraft. FAR 43 is included as Appendix II.

The FAA lists three primary maintenance processes. These processes are used to classify the maintenance process of each particular aircraft element involved. The primary maintenance processes are:

- ☐ *Overhaul time limit*—the process that requires the element be overhauled or removed from service at or prior to reaching a stated time limit.
- ☐ *On-condition maintenance*—preventive primary maintenance which requires that a system or part be periodically inspected against an appropriate physical standard to determine if the system or part should continue in service. The purpose of this inspection is to check for deterioration of the system or part.
- ☐ *Condition monitoring*—this process is for items that have no stated time limits and is accomplished by continuous monitoring of the system or part.

MAINTENANCE RECORDS

FAA regulations require that the owner or operator of an airplane keep detailed maintenance records on his/her airplane. These records should be transferred to the new owner when the aircraft is sold. Thus, the new owner should receive a complete maintenance history on the newly acquired aircraft.

A separate logbook is required for each engine, each airframe, and each propeller. Required entries in the logs include flight time, ground time, inspections, alterations, repairs, and maintenance performed.

For the recording of major repairs and major alterations, a FAA Form 337 (Major Repair and Alteration Form) must be used. One signed copy of the form becomes a part of the maintenance records of the aircraft and an additional signed copy is forwarded to the Aircraft Registry in Oklahoma City. A lost or misplaced form may be replaced by requesting a copy of the one on file at the Registry.

Accurate and complete maintenance records on an aircraft increase its market value, as they are a good indicator that the airplane has received proper maintenance care. In addition, accurate and complete maintenance records will assist an FAA inspector in determining that no unauthorized maintenance has been performed on the aircraft.

PREVENTIVE MAINTENANCE

Maintenance work on an aircraft must be either by, or under the supervision of, a licensed mechanic. Homebuilts and other experimental aircraft are not included in this requirement. An additional exception to this requirement is the preventive maintenance that may be accomplished by an aircraft owner or operator. For purposes of this exception, the owner or operator must be at least a Private Pilot and the aircraft must not be used as an air carrier.

Preventive maintenance means simple or minor preservation operations and the replacement of standard parts not involving complex assembly operations. It is corrective action taken before it becomes necessary to make a major repair.

FAA regulations require that the owner or operator who performs the preventive maintenance on his/her aircraft use only acceptable methods. In addition, tools and equipment necessary to assure proper and safe completion of the task are required. If special equipment is recommended by the manufacturer, the owner or operator is required to use that equipment or an equivalent substitute.

The following list of tasks comes under the heading of preventive maintenance and may be accomplished by the owner or operator:

1. Removal, installation, and repair of landing gear tires.
2. Replacing elastic shock absorber cords on landing gear.
3. Servicing landing gear shock struts by adding oil, air, or both.
4. Servicing landing gear wheel bearings, such as cleaning and adding grease.
5. Replacing defective safety wiring or cotter keys.

6. Lubrication not requiring disassembly other than removal of nonstructural items such as cover plates, cowlings, and fairings.

7. Making simple fabric patches not requiring rib stitching or the removal of structural parts or control surfaces.

8. Replenishing hydraulic fluids in the hydraulic reservoir.

9. Refinishing decorative coating of fuselage, wings, tail groups surfaces (except balanced control surfaces), fairings, cowlings, landing gear, cabin, or cockpit interior when removal or disassembly of any primary structure or operating system is not required.

10. Applying preservative or protective material to components where no disassembly of any primary structure or operating system is involved and where such coating is not prohibited or is not contrary to good practices.

11. Repairing upholstery and decorative furnishing of the cabin or cockpit interior when the repairing does not require disassembly of any primary structure or operating system or interfere with an operating system or affect primary structure of the aircraft.

12. Making small, simple repairs to fairings, nonstructural cover plates and cowlings, and small patches and reinforcements not changing the contour so as to interfere with proper airflow.

13. Replacing side windows where that work does not interfere with the structure or any operating system such as controls, electrical equipment, etc.

14. Replacing safety belts.

15. Replacing seats or seat parts with replacement parts approved for the aircraft not involving disassembly of any primary structure or operating system.

16. Troubleshooting and repairing broken circuits in landing light wiring circuits.

17. Replacing bulbs, reflectors, and lenses of position and landing lights.

18. Replacing wheels and skis where no weight and balance computation is involved.

19. Replacing any cowling not requiring removal of the propeller or disconnection of flight controls.

20. Replacing or cleaning spark plugs and setting of spark plug gap clearance.

21. Replacing any hose connection except hydraulic connections.

22. Replacing prefabricated fuel lines.

23. Cleaning fuel and oil strainers.

24. Replacing batteries and checking fluid level and specific gravity.

25. Removing and installing glider wings and tail surfaces that are designated for quick removal and installation when such installation can be accomplished by the pilot.

The above list is taken from Part 43-A, paragraph C of the FARs (see Appendix II in back of this book). Other tasks of a preventive maintenance nature may be undertaken by the pilot or owner. However, he/she should first obtain approval from a local FAA inspector. The aircraft's Airworthiness Certificate may be suspended for unauthorized maintenance.

AIRWORTHINESS DIRECTIVES

Airworthiness Directives, more commonly known as ADs, provide aircraft owners with information on unsafe conditions that may exist in their aircraft. These are published by the FAA when a defect is discovered which makes an aircraft unsafe and the condition is likely to exist or develop in other aircraft or aircraft components of the same type design.

The ADs specify the aircraft or component found to be unsafe and the conditions, limitations, or inspections (if any) under which the aircraft may continue to be operated. The FAA prior to issuing the AD considers the effectiveness of any operating restrictions (safety), the nature and amount of work involved for repair of the defect, the availability of replacement parts, and recommendations of the manufacturer and operators.

FAR 39.3 provides that no person may operate a product to which an Airworthiness Directive applies except in accordance with the requirements of that Directive.

It is the owner's responsibility to assure compliance with all ADs pertinent to his/her aircraft. This includes those ADs that require recurrent or continuing action. If the AD requires a certain type of inspection every 50 or 100 hours, it is the owner's responsibility to see that the AD is complied with and the fact of compliance is logged in the logbooks.

A chronological record is required to be maintained on all ADs on which action has been taken. The record must include the AD number, the date accomplished, a brief description of the method of compliance, and the signature and certificate number of the repair station or mechanic who complied with the AD. The record is normally maintained in the back of the appropriate logbook.

A summary of the Airworthiness Directives may be obtained from the FAR, Part 39 "Summary of Airworthiness Directives." Volume 1 is for aircraft whose empty weight is 12,500 pounds or less. Volume 2 is for large aircraft. This publication is updated yearly and may be obtained from the Superintendent of Documents, Government Printing Office, Washington, D.C. 20590.

For any ADs published on your aircraft since the yearly update, the summaries may be obtained from the FAA, Distribution Unit, HQ-438, Washington, D.C. 20553. An additional publication by the FAA which is a valuable tool to the aircraft owner is the *Personal Aircraft Inspection Handbook* (AC20-9) which may also be obtained from the Superintendent of Documents, or as TAB Book Number 2305 ($6.95), from TAB Books, Inc., Box 40, Blue Ridge Summit, PA 17214.

FAA INSPECTION AUTHORIZATION RATINGS

The primary responsibility of an Inspection Authorization inspector (IA) is to determine airworthiness of aircraft, components, etc., by inspecting repairs or alterations for conformity to approved data, and assuring that the aircraft is in a condition for safe operation.

Approving Major Repairs

An IA cannot delegate the authority to conduct inspections of major repairs; the IA must personally conduct the inspections. During the inspection for major repairs, the IA should make a detailed inspection to determine:

- ☐ The material used.
- ☐ Quality of workmanship.
- ☐ Compliance with approved data.
- ☐ Completeness of work.
- ☐ Possible overall effect on other structures or systems.

The signing of the aircraft records is considered by the courts as the assumption of responsibility for the safety aspects of the major repair. A completed FAA Form 337, Major Repair and Alteration, must also be completed.

Approval of Alterations

IAs cannot approve *data* for major alterations. They may, however, approve alterations that conform to data previously approved by FAA.

Annual and Progressive Inspections

The procedures and scope of Annual and Progressive Inspections are contained in FAR 43. (See Appendix II).

Qualifications

FAR Parts 43, 60, and 65 list the privileges and duties of mechanics holding an Inspection Authorization (IA). To qualify for the IA rating, the individual must hold a current Mechanic Certificate with both airframe and powerplant ratings. These ratings must be current and in effect for not less than three years immediately before the date of the application. Other requirements include: actively engaged in maintaining civil aircraft for at least two years prior to date of application; have a fixed base of operations where they can be located during the normal working week; have the necessary equipment, facilities and inspection data available to properly inspect aircraft and parts; and have passed a written test.

Application for IA

An applicant may apply for IA at the nearest FAA General Aviation District Office or at a Flight Standards District Office. An applicant is required to have available all the reference material needed for the test. The reference material required includes:

- ☐ FARs 1, 21, 23, 25, 33, 35, 39, 43, 45, 65, 91, and 183;
- ☐ Technical data as follows:

  (a) Aircraft Type Certificate Data Sheets and Specifications (AC 21-15 lists status of current requirements).

  (b) AC 43.13-1A (with changes 1 and 2)—Acceptable Methods, Techniques, and Practices, Aircraft Inspection and Repair.

  (c) AC 43.13-2A—Acceptable Methods, Techniques, and Practices—Aircraft Alterations.

  (d) Summary of Airworthiness Directives for Small Aircraft (Volume 1).

  (e) Summary of Airworthiness Directives for Large Aircraft (Volume 2).

- ☐ Advisory Circulars (ACs) 00, 10, 20, 60, 70, 90 and 120.

Actively Engaged

Applicants who are employed full-time in the maintenance of civil aircraft are considered as "actively engaged." Part-time employment must be evaluated and given consideration by an FAA airworthiness inspector.

Written Test

The written tests for the IA rating are given by appointment and normally take at least five hours. They are designed to test the ability of the applicant to use the proper technical data accurately while approving major repairs and alterations, and inspecting aircraft. Applicants need the ability to use the reference indexes quickly to locate specific information.

The test consists of three parts. Part 1 is a multiple choice type with a specific time limitation. The questions deal with the issuance, privileges, and limitations of the IA. Reference materials are not permitted to be used during part 1.

Parts 2 and 3 also have time limitations, but use of reference material is permitted. These parts cover situations applicants are likely to encounter while doing annual and progressive inspections or in approving major repairs and major alterations. During parts 2 and 3, the applicant is expected to use or to be familiar with the following:

- ☐ FARs pertaining to maintenance and airworthiness certification.
- ☐ Specifications of aircraft, engine, and propeller.

- ☐ Type Certificate data sheets on aircraft, engine, and propeller.
- ☐ Procedures for conducting annual and progressive inspections.
- ☐ Rules pertaining to the IA.
- ☐ Airworthiness Directives (ADs).

Duration of Ratings

IAs expire on March 31 of each year or when:

- ☐ The authorization is surrendered, suspended, or revoked.
- ☐ The holder no longer has a fixed base of operations.
- ☐ The holder no longer has the equipment, facilities, or inspection data needed.

Renewals

IAs are renewed at an FAA General Aviation, Flight Standards, or Air Carrier District Office during the month of March. For renewal, the IA must present evidence that the IA currently meets original requirements as set forth above.

Normally, renewals will be done in conjunction with safety meetings designed to help IAs increase their efficiency. The meetings usually include discussions on maintenance problems of a general nature, discussions of recent regulation changes and how the changes affect IAs, and discussions to acquaint IAs with new equipment and service problems.

IAs unable to attend scheduled meetings should contact the local FAA office during the month of March to determine the renewal procedures to be followed.

Here are some FAA suggestions for preventing problems between IAs and owners:

1. Make sure that the owner and you have a clear understanding of the work that is to be performed.
2. Itemize the work to be done to ensure that the owner will have a clear understanding as to the nature of the work involved.
3. Provide an estimate of the cost or range of costs anticipated. If costs exceed the estimate, notify the owner prior to incurring additional costs.
4. Advise the owner that, during annual inspections, determination of compliance with aircraft specifications and Airworthiness Directives must be checked.
5. Agree in advance as to whether any routine servicing is to be included as part of the inspection or is to be performed separately. Note that routine servicing is not a part of the inspection process.

6. Provide the owner with a written list of all discrepancies found on the aircraft and note whether or not each is corrected.
7. Set a reasonable time for completion of the work.
8. Request the owner to supply complete aircraft records (airframe, engine, and propeller logs).
9. Complete the inspection as soon as practicable.
10. Complete the necessary paperwork.

AIRWORTHINESS

The term *airworthy* is not defined in either the Federal Aviation Act or the Federal Aviation Regulations (FARs). Case law has defined "airworthy" to mean, first, that the aircraft conforms to its type design or certificate, and second, the aircraft is in a safe condition.

Conformity means no unauthorized changes, etc., and that the aircraft and its components are consistent with its Type Certificate. Safe condition refers to wear or deterioration status of the aircraft.

Notice of Unairworthy

A discrepancy list is to be provided to an aircraft owner with a copy to the local FAA General Aviation District Office or Flight Standards District Office when an airplane is found by an inspector to be in an unairworthy condition. A sample letter containing the list is set forth below:

> Mr. John J. Public
> 204 South Street
> Bangor, Maine 04403
>
> Dear Mr. Public:
>
> This is to certify that on September 30, 19XX, I completed an annual inspection on your aircraft, Cessna 140, N123456, S/N 54-22048 and found it to be in an unairworthy condition for the following reasons:
>
> 1. Maintenance records entry indicates that the engine had been overhauled but had not been approved for return to service as required by section 43.5 of the Federal Aviation Regulations.
> 2. Fabric on both horizontal stabilizers tests below allowable minimum of 56 pounds.
> 3. Number three cylinder compression checks below manufacturer's recommendations.
>
> Your aircraft will be considered to be in an airworthy condition when the above listed discrepancies have been corrected and

approved for return to service by a person authorized by Part 43
of the FARs.

George J. Jones
IA 123459
cc:
FAA General Aviation District Office

Sample Maintenance Record Entries

Below is a sample maintenance record for an annual inspection that resulted in an "airworthy" aircraft. Note: The date of inspection, total time, and the tach or recorder reading should be included. The inspector must sign the entry with his/her mechanic's certificate number.

> January 16, 19XX. Total aircraft time 1853.00 hours. Tach reading 983.0. Replaced right main wheel bearing, P/N 19844, upper bushing in R & L landing gear frames, both brake hoses, P/N 3402, and bled brakes. I certify that this aircraft has been inspected in accordance with an annual inspection and was determined to be in airworthy condition.
>
> George J. Jones
> IA 1234589

In addition to the above discrepancies letter, an entry is also made in the maintenance record when the airplane is found to be "unairworthy." Note that the date of inspection, total time, and tach reading are also included in the entry.

> January 16, 19xx. Total time 1853.00 hours. Tach reading 953.0. I certify that this aircraft had been inspected in accordance with an annual inspection and a list of discrepancies and unairworthy items dated (*insert date*) has been provided to the aircraft owner or lessee.
>
> George J. Jones
> IA 1234589

FERRY PERMITS

A *ferry permit* is a special flight authorization issued by FAA for an aircraft that does not currently meet the applicable aircraft airworthiness requirements, but is safe enough for the specific flight in question. A ferry permit is normally used to allow an airplane to be flown to another airport where repairs or alterations can be made on it or for flyaway delivery to a new owner.

Under a ferry permit, only the necessary crewmembers are allowed to fly in the airplane to its destination. When the trip is completed, the ferry permit must be returned to the local FAA official. A ferry permit is valid for only a limited period of time.

A ferry permit is obtained from an FAA office. The pilot or mechanic describes the mechanical condition of the aircraft and the reason that the aircraft needs to be ferried to another location. Prior to issuance of the permit, a licensed mechanic must certify that the aircraft is safe for its intended flight. The FAA does not normally inspect the aircraft before issuing the permit.

In one case, an experienced professional pilot was suspended for four months for her failure to obtain a ferry permit to fly an airplane from an obscure airstrip to a major airport after a damaged landing gear had been replaced by a licensed mechanic. In this case, the ferry permit would have been issued had it been applied for. The pilot had an outstanding safety record and over 20 years flight experience.

Chapter 6

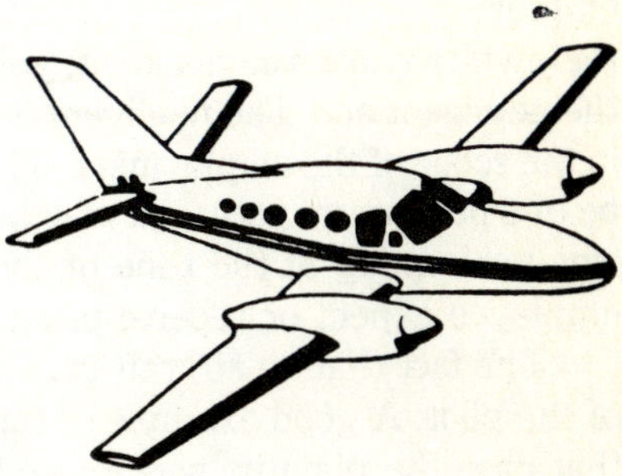

Negligence and Personal Liability

Pilot error or negligence is the leading cause of aviation accidents, according to a study by the FAA of over 15,000 general aviation accidents. In addition, "accident repeaters" (pilots who were involved in two or more accidents during the period under study) accounted for almost 10 percent of the total number of accidents surveyed.

One pilot, with more than 2,000 hours of experience, was involved in three major accidents during the period of study. The third accident was fatal for him. In the first accident, a hard landing caused major damage to the landing gear and both wings of his plane. His second accident resulted from lifting the airplane off the ground too soon and premature retraction of his landing gear. The third and final accident occurred when his aircraft crashed and burned seven miles from the airport. No malfunction or maintenance discrepancy was found. The pilot's blood alcohol content was high. He had a reputation of being ". . . lax regarding safe flight practices and allegedly flew while under the influence of alcohol on many occasions."

Another significant cause of aircraft accidents is negligence in maintenance.

PERSONAL LIABILITY

Personal liability is the claim for damages, etc., that may be made against an individual for bodily injury, death, or damage to property. Normally, personal liability arises as a result of negligent or willful acts or the failure to act when there is a duty to act on the part of the person concerned. An aircraft accident, for example, caused by the pilot's negligence may result in the personal liability of the pilot for any damages or injuries sustained. A similar situation may exist in the case of an aircraft renter who rents an aircraft that is not airworthy.

A person may also be held liable for the negligence or misconduct of his/her employees. If an employee of yours fills an aircraft with the wrong type of fuel, which causes an accident, you may be liable for any damages caused by the negligent act. The negligent act of the employee must, however, be within the scope of the employment. There is no requirement that this employment be of a permanent nature; it may be for only the single task that the employee was performing at the time of the negligence. It is not even necessary the employee expect or receive pay for the employment.

The fact that an aircraft crashes does not, by itself, establish negligence of the pilot. A good example of this rule is the case of *Flader v. Simonsen*; in that case the plaintiff was injured when a single-engine aircraft suffered a sudden engine and unexplained failure on takeoff and crashed. The Colorado Supreme Court dismissed the suit since the plaintiff failed to establish any negligence on the part of the pilot.

The general rule as recently stated by a federal district court in the Arrow Aviation Case is that pilots and owners are not insurers of their passengers' safety. Accordingly, the pilot or owner will not be held liable if the accident could not have been avoided. If, however, the accident is caused by the willful misconduct or negligence of the pilot or owner, in most cases the injured passengers may recover.

REASONABLE DEGREE OF CARE

When activities that can result in injuries or damages are performed for commercial reasons, a high degree of care is required of the aircraft owner or pilot. The term "degree of care" means the amount of care that the person concerned is expected to use if he/she is not to be considered as negligent. The owner or pilot engaged in aviation for noncommercial reasons (hobby) is required to exercise the degree of care an ordinarily prudent or reasonably careful person would use under the same or similar circumstances. The court looks back to the circumstances that resulted in the accident much the same way that a sports fan second-guesses a manager after the ballgame is lost. If the court determines after the backward glance that the actions of the pilot or owner were unreasonable or failed to meet a reasonable standard of care, then liability would arise.

One court has stated that the degree of care required is determined by state law. Thus, the degree may vary from state to state. While an act may make the pilot liable in one state, in another he may not be. Normally, the law of the state where the accident occurred will be the law for that case. However, if both the pilot and the injured persons are from one state and the accident occurred in another state, many states will apply the law of the state of their residence.

The standard of care required of pilots and owners of aircraft is as stated in one court case: "An aviator is under no duty to use the highest degree of care that men of reasonable diligence or foresight ordinary exercise in the operation of airplanes, but is bound to use ordinary care, although here, as in any other case, ordinary care differs under the circumstances. The care must be commensurate with the dangerous consequences to be reasonably apprehended; it must be a very high degree under some circumstances and of a slight degree under others." (Heitman v. Luhrs).

STANDARD OF CARE ESTABLISHED BY FARs

The numerous Federal Aviation Regulations (FARs) set forth in detail procedures to be used in most aviation-related activities. The courts have tended to view these FARs as establishing the reasonable standard of care to be used. For example, included as Appendix II is the FAR on preflighting an aircraft. It has been used by many courts to establish the standard of care that a reasonable person would use before flying an aircraft. Take a look at it. FARs also establish the standards of care that are generally applicable to all phases of the aviation industry.

PROXIMATE CAUSE

After a court finds the pilot or owner negligent, then, prior to holding him/her liable, it must also find that the negligent act caused the accident. For example, if the pilot failed to check the weather prior to a cross-country flight, but the accident was not caused by bad weather, the pilot's negligent act of not checking the weather would not make the pilot liable. If, however, the accident was caused by bad weather that the pilot should have been aware of, then the pilot would be liable since his/her negligent act was the proximate cause of the accident.

The requirement that the act of negligence must have caused the accident is labeled *proximate cause.* The courts have used many tests in determining if proximate cause exists. The most commonly used test is the "but for" test. Thus, if the accident would not have occurred "but for" the pilot's act of negligence, then the pilot is normally liable.

One court found that proximate cause existed in the death of a railroad employee. Evidence disclosed that the pilot was negligent in flying through a storm cloud. As a result, the pilot was forced to bail out. His ejected canopy fell and struck the railroad employee, who was eating lunch on the railroad right of way. The court held that but for the negligence of the pilot in flying through a storm cloud, the railroad worker would not have been killed.

If the act in question did not cause the accident, the pilot and/or owner may still be liable if their acts increased the damages or injuries. However, the person would be liable only for the added damages or injuries.

Also included in the proximate cause question is the test that the act of negligence in question must not be too remote from the accident. The remoteness is measured in events rather than in distance or time. Thus, an act of negligence separated by many other events would be considered too remote to hold the negligent person liable.

To illustrate the above remoteness rule, the classic case involving one Mrs. Palsgraft should be considered. Mrs. Palsgraft was injured and had a miscarriage when scales at a railway station in New York fell and hit her. It appears that as the train was leaving the Long Island Station, a male passenger was attempting to board the train. To assist him, a railroad worker pushed him on the train. As the passenger was pushed on the train, he dropped a package that was under his arm. The package contained firecrackers, which exploded. This caused sudden movement among the crowd and upset the scales, which then fell on Mrs. Palsgraft. The court found that the railroad employee was negligent in pushing the passenger on the train, but that the actual injury to Mrs. Palsgraft was too remote to hold the railroad liable.

PILOT NEGLIGENCE

The pilot-in-command is responsible for the safety of his/her aircraft and its passengers at all times. The negligent acts of the pilot may be grouped into four general areas: before takeoff, during takeoff, during flight, and during landing.

Some common acts for which a pilot has been held liable for negligence prior to takeoff include: failure to properly maintain and/or inspect aircraft, improper loading of aircraft, failure to conduct a complete preflight, and failure to check weather prior to takeoff (Fig. 6-1).

Some of the reported cases where pilots have been held liable for negligence on takeoffs are: misuse of brakes, faulty setting of propeller, improper position of flaps, takeoffs in the turbulent wake of a large aircraft, and failure to line up with runway lights when taking off during poor visibility.

Negligence during flight has been found to include: flying into bad weather, flying IFR conditions without a valid instrument ticket, running out of gas, flying into a tree, and flying at high altitude without an oxygen mask.

Negligence during landing has been found from: overshooting the runway on a gusty day, landing downwind, improper setting of propeller, turning with gear and flaps extended, crashing into wires and utility poles, landing at an unsafe field, and landing on a runway covered with a foot of snow when the *Airman's Information Manual* indicated that the field was not attended during winter months.

Even when landing at a controlled airfield, the pilot-in-command is primarily responsible for the safe operation of his/her aircraft in-flight or during ground movement. Clearances issued by a tower operator or air controller are considered permissive in nature and do not relieve the pilot from the duty to maintain a proper lookout. In one case, the pilot was held liable for an accident when the tower operator negligently cleared two planes to land on the same runway at the same time. The court reasoned that had the pilot maintained a proper

Form Approved OMB No 2120-0026

U S DEPARTMENT OF TRANSPORTATION FEDERAL AVIATION ADMINISTRATION **FLIGHT PLAN**	(FAA USE ONLY) ☐ PILOT BRIEFING ☐ VNR ☐ STOPOVER	TIME STARTED	SPECIALIST INITIALS

1 TYPE	2 AIRCRAFT IDENTIFICATION	3 AIRCRAFT TYPE/ SPECIAL EQUIPMENT	4 TRUE AIRSPEED	5 DEPARTURE POINT	6 DEPARTURE TIME PROPOSED (Z)	ACTUAL (Z)	7 CRUISING ALTITUDE
VFR							
IFR							
DVFR			KTS				

8 ROUTE OF FLIGHT

9 DESTINATION (Name of airport and city)	10 EST TIME ENROUTE HOURS	MINUTES	11 REMARKS

12 FUEL ON BOARD HOURS	MINUTES	13. ALTERNATE AIRPORT(S)	14 PILOT'S NAME, ADDRESS & TELEPHONE NUMBER & AIRCRAFT HOME BASE	15. NUMBER ABOARD
			17 DESTINATION CONTACT/TELEPHONE (OPTIONAL)	

16 COLOR OF AIRCRAFT	CIVIL AIRCRAFT PILOTS. FAR Part 91 requires you file an IFR flight plan to operate under instrument flight rules in controlled airspace. Failure to file could result in a civil penalty not to exceed $1,000 for each violation (Section 901 of the Federal Aviation Act of 1958, as amended). Filing of a VFR flight plan is recommended as a good operating practice. See also Part 99 for requirements concerning DVFR flight plans.

FAA Form 7233-1 (8-82) CLOSE VFR FLIGHT PLAN WITH ____________ FSS ON ARRIVAL

Fig. 6-1. FAA Flight Plan. Flight plans are required to be submitted for IFR flights. Pilots should also submit flight plans for any cross-country flights. Failure to file one on a long cross-country flight was considered as evidence of negligence by one court.

lookout, he could have avoided the accident. Accordingly, the pilot's negligence in failing to maintain proper lookout was a proximate cause of the accident.

Another case illustrates the responsibility of the pilot to maintain a proper lookout: In this case, the pilot maintained that his visibility while taxiing was limited due to design of the aircraft. The court, in holding the pilot responsible for the accident, stated that even though it may be difficult to maintain a lookout, this does not relieve the pilot of the responsibility, since he could either have had someone guide the aircraft from the ground or could have made S-turns while taxiing.

Other acts that have placed liability on the pilot include: taxiing in excess of 20 miles per hour, crossing an active runway, and failing to tie down an aircraft.

As you can surmise from the preceding cases, normally, a pilot is liable for his/her acts of negligence which are the proximate cause of the damages or injuries. However, several states have modified the common law rule to some extent. For example, one statute provides that the flight of an aircraft is lawful at proper altitude, but the pilot is charged with the responsibility of preventing injuries to persons and property beneath the aircraft. Under this statute, a pilot was held liable for injuries to a farmer when the farmer's team of mules were frightened by aircraft noise, even though no negligence on the part of the pilot was established.

AIRCRAFT OWNER

When the aircraft owner is not the pilot, he/she is not normally liable for the negligence of the pilot. In one case, for example, the owner was not held responsible for damages sustained by the negligent acts of the pilot where the aircraft was properly maintained and the pilot was qualified to fly the aircraft. The aircraft owner, however, is liable for allowing an unqualified pilot to operate the aircraft, i.e., negligent entrustment of the aircraft. In a similar situation, the owner was held responsible for allowing a pilot to rent his aircraft when the weather was below VFR minimums and the owner knew that the pilot did not possess a current instrument ticket.

When the owner is not the pilot, most courts do not make a distinction between an aircraft rented to the pilot and one loaned to the pilot. The general exception to this rule is where the aircraft has not been properly maintained. The aircraft rental owner is held to a higher standard of care as to the maintenance of his/her aircraft than the non-rental owner.

If the aircraft owner, in giving permission to use the aircraft, restricts the pilot's authority, in most cases the owner is not liable for injuries or damages caused if the pilot exceeds the restrictions. In one case, an aircraft owner loaned his aircraft to an inexperienced pilot. He instructed the pilot to fly only during daylight hours. The owner was held not liable for damages caused when the pilot crashed on landing at an unlighted airport at night. A similar rule applies when a pilot without the owner's knowledge flies into or takes off in bad weather.

The above rules are general ones and there are some states that hold the owner strictly liable for the negligence of the pilot under the assumption that the owner has provided the pilot with a hazardous piece of machinery. There also appears to be a trend toward holding the airplane owner liable for the negligent acts of the pilot based on the concept that the owner can easily insure the aircraft. In some states there are insurance requirements similar to those for automobiles, which require the owner or operator of an aircraft to have liability insurance that covers the pilot as well as the owner.

California is one of those states that place absolute liability on the owner for the negligence of the pilot. This appears to be the trend among states for insurance purposes. The California statute (Public Utilities Code, section 21404) provides:

> Every owner of an aircraft is liable and responsible for death or injury to person or property resulting from a negligent or wrongful act or omission in the operation of the aircraft, in the business of the owner

> or otherwise, by any person using or operating the same with a permission, express or implied of the owner.

Most of those states with similar statutes exclude the owner from the above when the aircraft is leased to any party for periods in excess of 30 days, and those who only hold legal title as a security interest for payment of a debt.

Note: The pilot is responsible to the owner for any damages caused to the airplane by the negligence of the pilot.

The owner is responsible for the proper care of his/her aircraft and can be held liable for any damages or injuries resulting either from faulty maintenance or failure to have the airplane inspected at the required intervals.

LIABILITY OF AIRLINES

The rules discussed above regarding the responsibilities of the owner or pilot of an aircraft are modified in those cases where commercial airlines are involved. Since an airline is a "common carrier" and holds itself out to the public as willing to carry passengers for hire indiscrimately.

A common carrier is held to a very high standard of care regarding its passengers. The rules of care are the same as the degree of care required on a common carrier on land, such as a Greyhound Bus. Note: While requiring the highest degree of care for the safety of its passengers, the general rule is that the airline is not an insurer of the safety of the passengers.

When a commercial airlines airplane is involved in an accident, the doctrine of *res ipsa loquitur* normally applies. This doctrine provides that where an instrumentality involved in an accident is within the exclusive control of the defendant and where the accident is one which would ordinarily not have happened in the absence of negligence, then the jury or court may infer negligence from the mere happening of the accident. Thus, when an airliner crashes, since it is under the exclusive control of the defendant (airline company), the jury may infer that the airline company employees (pilot, etc.) were negligent. The reason for this rule is that it is easier for the airline company to provide the cause of the accident than it would be for the person suing the airlines.

NEGLIGENCE PER SE

There are several situations where the courts usually determine that the person involved is negligent *per se* (speaks for itself). Some of those are listed below. Note: The act in question must also be the cause in fact of the accident.

- ☐ Violation of Federal Aviation Regulations—The FAA regulations are admissible in evidence to establish the standard of care that a pilot/owner should exercise. For example, failure to follow FAA maintenance regulations may constitute negligence *per se* when an aircraft accident is caused by aircraft mechanical failure.

- ☐ Flying too low.
- ☐ Failure to keep aircraft under proper control.
- ☐ Intentionally flying into a storm.
- ☐ Failure to conform with air traffic patterns.
- ☐ Failure to maintain, inspect, and overhaul aircraft.
- ☐ Overloading aircraft.

DEFENSES

There are several defenses that a pilot, owner, etc., may use to avoid liability in addition to the general denial of "no negligence." The most common ones are lack of causation, assumption of risk, contributory negligence, and act of God. Each of these will be discussed in this section.

Assumption of Risk

The "assumption of the risk" defense is not a favored defense with the courts. In general, this defense is that when a person knowingly and willingly accepts a risk, that person should not be able to complain of the natural consequences of the act. For this to apply, the other party must establish that the injured person knew of the risks involved completely and appreciated the gravity of the situation. This may apply where two pilots knowing of the mechanical condition of an aircraft fly it anyway and it crashes. It would not apply to cases where the injured party is not knowledgeable in the area, i.e., a non-pilot who is not aware of the importance of aircraft maintenance.

In one case in which the pilot and his passenger flew into a weather front, the court held that the passenger had assumed the risk since he (also a pilot) was present at the weather briefing and was informed in advance of the poor weather conditions and advised not to go.

Many states have restricted the use of this defense. A New York statute (Section 1411, NY Civil Practice Law) for example, provides:

> In any action to recover damages for personal injury, injury to property, or wrongful death, the including contributory negligence or assumption of the risk, shall not bar recovery, but the amount of damages otherwise recoverable shall be diminished in the proportion which the culpable conduct attributable to the claimant or decedent bears to the culpable conduct which caused the damages.

Statutes of this type limit the assumption of the risk defense only to the amount of damages caused by the actions of the person injured.

Contributory Negligence

Contributory negligence was a complete defense at common law. The general nature of this defense is that the person who was injured was also negligent and the his/her negligence was a contributing factor to the accident. An example of this would be the case of a pilot who is injured when his aircraft crashes due to lack of fuel. The pilot, prior to takeoff, had been informed by the fixed base operator that the plane had recently been refueled. In this case, the fixed base operator was negligent in incorrectly advising the pilot of the fuel level in the aircraft. The pilot, however, would have problems recovering since he was also negligent in not ascertaining the fuel status prior to takeoff. Accordingly, the pilot was contributorily negligent.

In many states, the common law defense has been modified by the comparative negligence rule. Note the New York statute set forth above is a common statutory modification. In those states, the negligence of the injured person does not prevent him/her from recovering, but reduces the amount of recovery. The jury would be asked to determine the degree of fault of each party involved. If the total damages, for example, are $100,000 and one party is 70 percent responsible for the accident and the other is 30 percent, then the first party would be required to shoulder $70,000 of the loss and the other would be required to shoulder $30,000 of the loss.

Act of God

The Act of God defense was recognized at common law as a complete defense to a claim for damages. An act of God would be a sudden thunderstorm with no warning, etc. It is, in effect, a finding that the accident was not caused by negligence but by an uncontrollable and unexpected force of nature.

Latent Defect

A *latent defect* is a defect that caused the accident, but such defect was not discoverable even with the exercise of utmost care on the part of the pilot/owner, etc. Accordingly, there was no negligence on the part of the pilot/owner.

Contribution and Indemnification

If a person who is partly responsible for an accident is required to pay the total cost of the damages, that party has a right to recover a portion of the cost from third parties whose negligence was also partly responsible for the loss. The courts have held that the right of contribution between parties who have caused a loss should be shared between the parties based on responsibility, fairness, and the facts of the case.

GUEST STATUTES

As of 1986, 30 states had "guest" statutes limiting the liability of owners or operators of automobiles or vehicles who were not liable for injuries or damages to guest passengers in cases involving simple negligence. Guests are defined as passengers who give no compensation for their ride.

The question in those states is, do those same statutes apply to aircraft? The general rule is that airplanes are not considered within the definition of vehicles for the purposes of the guest statutes. As one court stated, "The word 'vechile' is commonly meant as a vehicle that operates upon land." Currently, 13 states by either statute or court decisions have applied "guest statutes" to aviation. Three states—California, Utah, and Michigan—have held that "guest statutes" are unconstitutional. The 13 states that have a guest statute that applies to aviation are: Arkansas, Delaware, Idaho, Illinois, Indiana, Nebraska, New Mexico, North Dakota, Ohio, Oregon, South Carolina, and South Dakota.

There are eleven states whose guest statutes do *not* apply to aircraft. These states are Alabama, Colorado, Florida, Iowa, Kansas, Montana, Texas, Vermont, Virginia, Washington, and Wyoming.

In one interesting federal court case involving a collision between two aircraft both owned by the same individual, the court held that the guest statute did not prevent the guest from suing the owner of the other airplane, even though he was also owner of the host aircraft.

The guest statutes do not apply if the pilot benefits in a commercial sense from the passenger's travel. Thus, where the purpose of the trip was to arrange transactions as a joint venture for the establishment of a nursing home, the court held that the passengers were not guests since there was a commercial purpose for their trip and therefore the passengers could sue the pilot for simple negligence. Note: Guest statutes do not apply to those cases where the pilot was grossly negligent. Its purpose is to prevent persons to whom the pilot gives a courtesy ride form suing the pilot for simple negligence.

DUAL CONTROL AIRCRAFT

In those cases where the airplane has dual controls and both persons in the front seats are pilots, a difficult question arises as to which pilot is in control or is the pilot-in-command. If one is a licensed pilot and the other is a student pilot, there is an assumption that the licensed pilot is the pilot-in-command. A similar situation exists if one pilot is giving instructions to the other pilot. The fact that one pilot has more experience or a higher rating (except as noted above) does not raise the presumption that the pilot with more experience or a higher rating is in command.

As one court stated, the imposition of liability on either pilot would be purely speculative and conjectural where both occupants of the aircraft were capable of flying it alone and there was no evidence to establish which of them was flying the plane at the time of the accident, or who was negligent.

Note: Since in most small airplanes with side-by-side seating and dual controls, while it is customarily for the pilot to be seated on the left side, it is not required. Accordingly, the fact that one pilot was in the left seat and the other was in the right seat is not considered as evidence as to which was flying at the time of the accident.

Some states, such as Nebraska, impose no presumption of responsibility on the pilot-in-command when both persons are capable of legally operating the aircraft.

In one Missouri case, the owner of the airplane was seated on the left side of the aircraft at the time it crashed. The court state that since the pilot is normally seated on the left and in this case the owner was in that seat, the jury could find that the owner was also the operator of the aircraft when the accident occurred. The court in this case noted that FAR 91.3 provides "the pilot-in-command of the aircraft shall be directly responsible for its operation and shall have final authority as to the operation of the aircraft."

To eliminate the above problem, at least one state (Ohio) has a statute designed to eliminate the problem. Ohio Revised Code, Section 4561.23 provides (in part):

> In the event of an airplane crash involving personal injuries, death or property damage, it is rebuttably presumed that the airplane was being flown at the time of the crash, and immediately prior thereto, by the pilot-in-command of such airplane when the airplane is occupied by more than one person.
>
> The pilot in command is rebuttably presumed to be:
>
> (a) The occupant of the left front seat in airplanes having side by side and fore and aft seating;
>
> (b) The occupant of the left seat of an airplane which has only one transverse seat;
>
> (c) In a tandem seat airplane, the occupant of the seat recommended by the manufacturer of such airplane when the airplane is flown solo;
>
> (d) Notwithstanding divisions (a), (b), and (c) of this section, the occupant of the airplane possessed of an instructor's rating is rebuttably presumed to be the pilot-in-command when any part of the flight is for the purposes of instructing another in any phase of flying or navigating.
>
> (e) Notwithstanding divisions (a), (b), (c), or (d) of this section, in all flights conducted under instrument flight rules, the pilot-in-command is rebuttably presumed to be the pilot whose name appears on the flight plan.
>
> (f) In the event that the occupants and their positions in the airplane at the time of the crash can not be established otherwise from the evidence with reasonable certainty, it is presumed that the airplane was being flown at the time of the crash and immediately prior thereto, by the person occupying the pilot-in-command seat, as designed above, during or immediately before takeoff.

LIABILITY OF FEDERAL GOVERNMENT

When an employee of the federal government is negligent and the negligence is within the scope of the employee's employment with the federal government, the injured person may in certain cases recover from the federal government. The principal basis for liability is the Federal Tort Claims Act.

The Act provides that federal district courts have exclusive jurisdiction of civil actions on claims against the United States.

In most cases, the claimant must first file an administrative claim against the U.S. The claim should be filed with the agency or federal department involved. There is a standard form for filing the claim. After the claim has been denied, then the individual may sue in district court. If the agency or department to which the claim is filed has not acted on the claim within six months, then the claimant may consider that the claim was denied and file suit in district court.

General rules regarding the Federal Tort Claims Act are:

- ☐ Must be in scope of employment.
- ☐ Injury or damage must occur within the geographical limits of the U.S.
- ☐ Does not apply to combat activity.
- ☐ Does not apply to discretionary functions of federal officials.
- ☐ Military persons on active duty cannot be claimants under the Act.
- ☐ The statute of limitations is two years.
- ☐ There is no right to a jury trial in claims under the Act.

Military Claims Act

An act very similar to the Federal Tort Claims Act is the Military Claims Act, which provides coverage where the accident is the result of military activity in which there has been no negligence on the part of a government employee.

Air Traffic Controllers

The liability of air traffic controllers for negligence in directing aircraft is discussed in Chapter 11.

Liability of Government Inspectors or Examiners

No reported case could be found where the government was held liable for the negligent inspection of an aircraft. It would appear that if negligence could be established and that the negligence was the proximate cause of the accident, recovery would be appropriate. Note: Awards have been upheld against the federal government for negligent inspections in non-aviation activities (FmHA housing cases). Also, a non-government person has been held liable for the negligent inspection of an aircraft.

PERSONS AND PROPERTY ON THE GROUND

In this section, the liability of pilots and aircraft owners for injuries to persons and damages to property on the ground will be discussed. Many states have statutes imposing absolute liability on owners and pilots of aircraft for deaths, injuries, or damages caused to persons on the ground. Other states have held against the owners and pilots in these situations based on the concept that the intrusion on the land of another by falling objects is a common law trespass. In either case, negligence is not necessary in order to recover.

In the remainder of the states, it appears that negligence must be established on the part of the pilot or owner before recovery will be allowed. As one court stated, "There can be no trespass absent an intent to crash."

Several states, such as Maryland, have a statute that creates a presumption of negligence when an airplane crashes or when objects fall from an airplane. Under this type of situation, the pilot/owner would be required to prove an absence of negligence to prevent recovery.

AIRCRAFT MANUFACTURERS

The general rule is that aircraft manufacturers are liable for the faulty design or faulty manufacture of the aircraft or aircraft parts. There is a similar duty of a manufacturer to warn users of its airplanes or airplane parts of known dangerous conditions or characteristics. This duty continues after the aircraft or products are sold. In addition, the manufacturer has a duty to inform the FAA so that an airworthiness directive may be issued if appropriate. The leading case on the duty to warn is the case of Noel v. United Aircraft Corp. In that case, the court stated: "A manufacturer is under a continuing duty to improve its product where human safety is involved. It is clear that after such a product has been sold and dangerous defects in design have come to the manufacturer's attention, the manufacturer has a duty to either remedy these or, if complete remedy is not feasible, at least to give users adequate warnings and instructions for minimizing the danger."

ROLE OF FARS

Most courts will allow the admission into evidence of applicable Federal Aviation Regulations in civil ligation involving aviation cases. The regulations may be used by the jury or a judge as to the proper standard of care that should be exercised in the fact situation. In some cases, the courts have held that if the injured party established that the defendant has violated an FAR and that this was the proximate cause of the accident, then the defendant is negligent *per se* (considered as negligent without additional evidence). Other courts hold that violation of an FAR is not negligence *per se*, but is strong evidence of negligence.

If there is a conflict between FARs and state law, then the FARs prevail. The fact that state law and an FAR prohibit the reckless operation of an aircraft is not a conflict and in some cases, the pilot may be tried in state criminal court for violation of the state law prohibiting the reckless operation of an aircraft and also given sanction by the FAA for the violation of the FAR. A conflict between a state statute and a federal regulation is present only when there is a direct conflict. A situation such as this occurs only where the pilot, etc., in obeying one, violates the other. In most cases, the state statute or regulation and the FAR are considered as complementary to each other.

Chapter 7

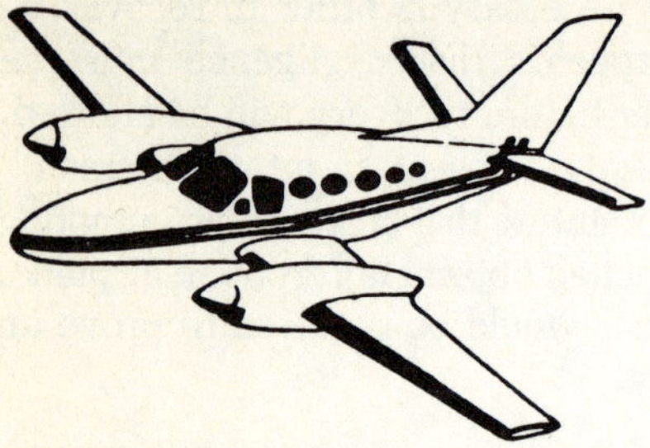

Aircraft Accidents, Investigations, and Enforcement

In this chapter, the reporting, investigation of accidents, and enforcement of FAA rules and regulations will be discussed (Fig. 7-1). In addition, procedures and rights at NTSB hearings will be examined.

REPORTING ACCIDENTS

The operator of an aircraft is required to immediately notify the nearest National Transportation Safety Board, Bureau of Aviation Safety Field Office, when:

1. An aircraft accident or any of the following listed incidents occurs:
   a. Flight control system malfunction or failure.
   b. In-flight fire.
   c. Aircraft collision in flight.
   d. Turbine engine failure.
   e. Inability of any required crew-member to perform his/her normal flight duties as a result of injury or illness.
2. An aircraft is overdue and believed to have been involved in an accident.

The following information is required to be reported if available:

- ☐ Location.
- ☐ Date/time.

FORM APPROVED O.M.B. No. 004–R–0176

DEPARTMENT OF TRANSPORTATION
FEDERAL AVIATION ADMINISTRATION
SAFETY IMPROVEMENT REPORT

This report is authorized by law (49 U.S.C. 1421) while you are not required to respond, your cooperation is needed to make the results of this survey comprehensive, accurate and timely.

PURPOSE: To invite your participation in The General Aviation Accident Prevention Program. This form is provided for you to offer ideas for program improvement or to report hazards to aviation safety that you may have observed. Examples of hazards are: obstructions or other hazards on or adjacent to airport traffic patterns; incomplete, inaccurate or obsolete flight data (charts or publications); malfunctioning navigation aids; contaminated fuel; etc. This report is not intended to be used to report violations of Federal Aviation Regulations.

USE THE SPACE BELOW TO TELL US ABOUT YOUR PROGRAM IDEAS OR ABOUT A HAZARD THAT MIGHT CAUSE AN ACCIDENT.
(If you are reporting a hazard, tell us what it is, where it is located, and when it was noticed.)

DATE	YOUR NAME AND ADDRESS *(Optional)*

FAA FORM 8740–5 (3–80) FORMERLY FAA FORM 8000–7 (2–71)

Fig. 7-1. As part of the Safety Improvement Program of the FAA, SIRs (Safety Improvement Reports) are used by pilots to report safety hazards. Note: This report is not to be used to report violations of FARs.

☐ Aircraft make, model, and registration number.
☐ Names of operators, crew, and passengers.
☐ Number of persons involved.
☐ Injuries to each person.
☐ Weather conditions.
☐ Known witnesses.

The nearest NTSB may be notified by contacting the local FAA facility, which will in turn notify the Safety Board. The initial notification may be by telephone.

Within 10 days after the accident or reportable incident, the operator is required to file a written notice with the NTSB using the accident report form NTSB 6120. Each crewmember is required to attach to the form, submitted by the operator, a statement setting forth the facts and circumstances relating to the accident or incident as known to him/her. The required report form may be obtained from the local FAA facility.

Not all aircraft mishaps are considered to be accidents by the Safety Board. Thus, if the mishap does not meet their definition of an accident and does not involve any of the earlier mentioned incidents, there is no requirement to report it. Note: Some states have reporting requirements in addition to those required by the FARs. For purposes of reporting requirements by the NTSB, an accident is defined as an occurrence which occurs during the starting or warming up of an engine or the operation of an aircraft and causes either fatal or serious injuries or substantial damage to an aircraft.

Serious or fatal injuries resulting from contact with a rotating propeller which is installed on an aircraft is considered by the Board as a reportable accident.

Fatal injuries are any injuries which result in death within seven days. Serious injuries are any injuries which meet one of the below qualifications:

- ☐ Requires hospitalization for more than 48 hours, commencing within seven days from the date the injuries were sustained.
- ☐ Results in the fracture of any bone except a simple fracture of fingers, toes or the nose.
- ☐ Involves lacerations which cause severe hemorrhages, nerve, muscle, or tendon damage.
- ☐ Involves injuries to any internal organs.
- ☐ Involves second or third-degree burns, or any burns affecting more than five percent of the body surface.

Substantial damage to an aircraft with a gross weight of 12,500 pounds or less is defined for reporting purposes as damage or structural failure reasonably estimated to cost $300 or more to repair. Engine failure and damages limited to an engine are not considered an accident, unless the damage to the aircraft excluding the engine exceeds $300.

HOMEBUILT AIRCRAFT

Any accident involving a homebuilt aircraft must be reported regardless of the amount of damage or the nature of the injuries involved. This is an exception to the above rules.

STATE NOTIFICATION

As noted earlier, the majority of states require the aircraft operator to notify either the local police or sheriff's office when an aircraft accident occurs. Virginia, for example, requires the operator to notify the local police when an aircraft accident occurs which results in damage to the aircraft in excess of $200 or in serious or fatal injuries. In California, the monetary damage amount is $400. Thus, as a matter of routine, the operator should notify the local police or sheriff's office immediately after the FAA is informed.

NOTIFICATION TO INSURANCE COMPANY

As discussed in Chapter 8, insurance policies require the operator to notify the insurance company within a required number of days after the accident, regardless of the degree of fault involved. Failure to notify within the required time is considered as a breach of the insurance contract and may be basis for the insurance company to refuse to pay under the policy. An early notification allows the insurance company to conduct its own investigation while the evidence is available. Since the insurance company is required to protect your financial interest, it is necessary that you cooperate with its investigator.

FAA INVESTIGATIONS

As noted in Chapter 1, the FAA investigates on behalf of the NTSB civil aircraft accidents involving aircraft which have a maximum gross takeoff weight of 12,500 pounds or less, except for those accidents involving fatal injuries. The NTSB investigates the accidents involving aircraft whose take-off weight exceeds 12,500 pounds and those involving fatal injuries.

When the FAA investigates an accident, their responsibilities include:

- ☐ To determine if there is a violation of an FAR.
- ☐ To determine if the airworthiness of an FAA-certificated aircraft is involved.
- ☐ To determine if the performance of the FAA certificated airmen, air agencies, commercial operators, or air carriers is involved.
- ☐ To determine if the competence of FAA facilities or personnel is involved.

The FAA report, which is forwarded to the NTSB, does not include any findings as to the civil liability of the pilot or owner for damages or injuries arising out of the accident. Nor can the report be used in a court of law by injured parties suing either the owner or the pilot. However, in certain cases, the FAA investigator may be called as an expert witness on the cause of the accident during the litigation. The right to call FAA personnel, however, is currently limited by federal regulations.

If the investigation discloses that FAA regulations were violated, then the enforcement procedures noted later in this chapter may apply.

ENFORCEMENT PROCEDURES

Any person who is aware of an FAA rule violation may report this fact by telephone to the nearest FAA facility. If possible, the name of the pilot and the aircraft registration number should be included in the violation report. The local FAA facility will normally forward the report to the nearest regional or district office, where it is subject to investigation by a field inspector. A letter similar to the sample letter in the latter part of Chapter 8 will be sent to the pilot or owner under investigation.

If, from the investigation, it appears that the actions of the pilot or owner did not violate any rules, then the matter is dismissed. If the inspector concludes that the violation was minor and unintentional, he/she may issue a letter entitled "Warning Notice of Violation." A copy of this letter is sent to the pilot or owner concerned and a copy is retained for FAA records. This notice closes the matter.

When it appears that the violation is minor but due to the intentional or negligent actions of the person involved, the inspector may recommend to the Regional or Area Counsel that a "Letter of Reprimand" be issued. This letter is considered as a disciplinary measure, whereas the "Warning Notice of Violation" is corrective in nature. While a letter of reprimand closes the matter under investigation, the letter is noted on the offender's record of license and may be used against him/her in any future investigations involving the same individual.

Serious violations of FAA rules or of the Federal Aviation Act may be punished by civil penalties not to exceed a fine of $1,000. In addition, the aircraft involved may be seized and the aircraft's and airman's certificates suspended or revoked. In appropriate cases, any violations may be referred to the Department of Justice for criminal prosecution. If criminal prosecution is used, the case, if minor, will be tried before a federal magistrate; if considered major (a felony), it will be tried in a U.S. District Court. The defendant in these cases will have the right to be represented by an attorney and a jury trial.

Except in unusual cases, before an aircraft or airman certificate is suspended or revoked, the Regional or Area FAA Counsel notifies the person (or persons) involved. The person is informed of the charges against him/her or other grounds on which the proposed action is based and the type of action proposed. This notification is in the form of a letter and entitled "Notice of Proposed Certificate Action." By checking the appropriate box on the lower portion of the letter, the person involved may either:

- ☐ Admit the charge and surrender the certificate in question.
- ☐ Answer the charges in writing.
- ☐ Request an informal conference with the Regional or Area Counsel.
- ☐ Request a formal hearing.

If the notice letter is not returned within 15 days with the appropriate box marked, the action proposed in the letter is taken. If an informal conference is requested with the Regional or Area FAA Counsel and the person involved is not satisfied with the results, the person may request within 10 days after close of the informal conference a formal hearing.

At the formal hearing, the certificate holder has a right to be represented by an attorney—and normally should be. The formal hearing, like most administrative hearings, resembles a court trial in many respects. It is conducted by a hearing officer (Administrative Law Judge) with similar powers to those of a judge presiding over a court case. The person involved (interested party) has a right to an impartial hearing.

Enforcement of Orders

If the person charged with a violation is assessed a civil penalty, the individual has 60 days to pay the assessment. If not paid within the 60 days, the matter can then be referred to the U.S. Attorney General for collection activity in U.S. District Court. The officer who assessed the penalty may for good cause grant an extension of time to pay the penalty. In addition, the amount of any assessed civil penalty may be compromised at any time prior to its referral with the Attorney General's Office. Note: Once referred to the Attorney General's Office, it can be compromised by that office also.

Seizure of Aircraft

The Federal Aviation Act (section 903) authorizes a state or federal law enforcement officer or an FAA safety inspector to seize an aircraft pursuant to seizure orders issued by the Regional Director for that region or by the Chief Counsel. The person seizing the aircraft has a duty to place it in the nearest available and adequate public storage facility in the judicial district in which it was seized.

The Regional Director or Chief Counsel is then required without delay to send a written notice and copy of Part 13.17 of Federal Aviation Regulations (also published as Code of Federal Regulations Title 14, part 13.17) to the registered owner of the seized aircraft and to any other interested party. The notice should state:

- ☐ Time, date and place of seizure.
- ☐ Name and address of the custodian of the aircraft.
- ☐ Reasons for the seizure, including violations believed, or judicially determined, to have been committed.
- ☐ Amount that may be tendered as
  - a. civil penalty that has been judicially imposed for a violation, or
  - b. a compromise of civil penalty for the alleged violation.

Next, the Counsel notifies the Office of the U.S. Attorney for the judicial district in which the aircraft was seized, requesting that the attorney institute proceedings to enforce a lien against the aircraft.

The Regional Director or Chief Counsel should direct the release of the seized aircraft whenever:

- ☐ The civil penalty or amount agreed upon in compromise and the costs of seizing, storing and maintaining the aircraft, have been paid.

- ☐ The aircraft is seized under an order of a federal court and the order is rescinded or the U.S. Attorney notifies the FAA that no further proceedings will be taken in the case.
- ☐ A bond in the amount and with the sureties prescribed by Chief Counsel or the Regional Director is deposited, conditioned on payment of the penalty, or the compromise amount plus costs of seizing, storing, and maintaining aircraft.

Certificate Action

Under the Federal Aviation Act (section 609), the FAA may re-inspect any civil aircraft, aircraft engine, propeller, appliance, air navigation facility, or air agency, and may re-examine any civil airman. The certificate in question may be suspended or revoked for any cause that renders the aircraft ineligible for registration.

As the results of the inspection, if a determination is made that public interest and safety require it, an order will be issued amending, suspending, or revoking all or part of any certificate. The holder of the certificate or interested party has the right to request a formal hearing as noted above.

Orders of Compliance

Unless sooner action is required for reasons of safety, the FAA will provide 30 days notice of any orders of compliance, cease and desist orders. The interested person may within 10 days of being notified of the proposed action request a formal hearing. Failure to request a hearing constitutes a waiver of this right to a hearing and also the right to appeal.

Rules of Practice for Formal Hearings

If a person has the right to request a hearing, the person may appear and be heard in person or represented by attorney.

A request for hearing must be submitted in writing to the Hearing Docket, Room 914 E, Federal Aviation Administration, 800 Independence Avenue S.W., Washington, D.C. 20591 (unless notice sent to interested party indicates a different address). The request must describe briefly the action proposed by FAA and contain a statement that a hearing is requested. A copy of the notice must be served on the official who issued the notice of proposed action.

In addition, an answer (reply) to the notice of proposed action must be filed with the request for a hearing. Any allegation in the notice not specifically denied is deemed admitted. Note: In answering any notice, care should be taken to ensure that any allegation that will be contested at the hearing must be specifically mentioned and denied. For example, a statement such as "The undersigned interested party hereby denies the allegations contained in paragraphs 3, 5, and 6 in that the person did in fact have a valid Medical and Private Pilot Certificates in his possession at the time of the incident in question on May 24, 19XX at 3:00 P.M. The undersigned person attempted to present the Medical and Private Pilot Certificates to the inspector, but the inspector failed to give the opportunity to do so" is the type of statement that should be contained in the answer.

Within 15 days after receiving service of the copy of request for hearing, the official who issued the notice is required to forward a copy of the notice to the Hearing Docket. The notice serves as the complaint (charge) at the hearing.

Powers and duties of the hearing officer are:

- ☐ Give notice concerning, and hold, prehearing conferences and hearings.
- ☐ Administer oaths and affirmations.
- ☐ Examine witnesses.
- ☐ Adopt procedures for the submission of evidence in written form.
- ☐ Issue subpoenas and take depositions or cause them to be taken.
- ☐ Rules on offers of proof.
- ☐ Receive evidence.
- ☐ Hold conferences before and during the hearing to settle and simplify issues by consent of the parties.
- ☐ Dispose of procedural requests and similar matters.
- ☐ Issue decisions, make finding of fact, make assessments, and issue orders as appropriate.

Copies of all documents filed with the Hearing Docket must be served on all parties to the proceedings by the person filing them. Service may be made by personal delivery or by mail.

On written request and for good cause shown, a Hearing Officer may grant an extension of time to file any documents.

At any time more than 10 days prior to the hearing date, any party may amend or change his or her notice, answer, etc., by filing the amendment with the Hearing Officer and serving a copy on each interested party. In addition, the FAA or the interested party may withdraw the notice or request for hearing.

Motions

The following motions may be submitted by the parties:

1. Motion to dismiss for insufficiency—Normally made to dismiss for failure of the notice to state a violation of regulations or statutes, etc.
2. Motion for a more definite statement—Made by a party to require that the allegations be made more specific. If granted by the Hearing Officer, the other party has 10 days to file an amendment.
3. Motion for judgment of the pleadings—Made when the opposing party's pleadings admit sufficient facts to establish either the violation, etc, or lack of violation.

4. Motion to strike—On motion of any party, the hearing officer may order stricken from any pleading, any insufficient allegation or defense, or any immaterial, impertinent, or scandalous matter.

5. Motion for discovery—Upon motion by any party with a showing of good cause, the hearing officer may order any other party to produce any designated document, photograph, object, or other tangible object.

Answers to motions may be filed by any party contesting the motion within five days after the party has been served with a copy of the motion.

Intervention

Any person who can establish that he/she has a property or financial interest that may not be adequately represented by existing parties, and that the intervention will not unduly broaden or delay the proceedings, may be allowed to intervene by the hearing officer. The request for intervention is normally made to the hearing officer and should state the reasons that intervention is necessary to protect the interests of the party requesting it.

A request to intervene may not be considered if it is filed less than 10 days before the hearing.

Depositions

After a request for a formal hearing is filed by the respondent and an answer, either party may take testimony by deposition. The deposition is taken under oath and transcribed by a court reporter. The other party must be given notice of the taking of a deposition and afforded the opportunity to cross-examine the witness. In many cases, a deposition is used in lieu of the appearance of the witness at the formal hearing.

Notice of Hearing

The hearing officer sets the date, time, and place for the hearing and is required to provide adequate notice to all parties concerned. A hearing officer should give due regard to the convenience of the parties. In addition, for good cause the hearing officer can change the hearing date, time, or place.

Subpoenas and Witness Fees

On application of a party, the hearing officer may issue subpoenas requiring the attendance of witnesses or the production of documentary or other evidence at the hearing. The application for producing evidence must state the general relevance and reasonable scope of the evidence.

If the witness requested is an employee of the FAA, the application must be in writing and set forth the need for that employee's attendance.

Witnesses are entitled to the same fees and travel expenses as a witness in a federal court. The party requesting the witness is required to pay the costs associated with the witness's attendance. The hearing officer may waive witness costs to any party if that party can establish a serious hardship if required to pay the costs.

Evidence

Each party may present evidence, oral or documentary, to further the party's contentions. The burden of proof to establish the misconduct, etc., of a party is upon the FAA counsel.

Arguments

The hearing officer is required to give the parties adequate opportunity to present arguments in support of their contentions. The hearing officer makes the determination whether oral or written shall be submitted. In addition, each party may submit written proposed findings and conclusions and supporting reasons for them.

Record of Hearing

All testimony and exhibits presented at a hearing, together with all papers and documents filed in the proceedings, constitute the record and shall be the exclusive basis for the issuance of any order by the hearing officer. Any party may obtain a transcript of the record from the official reporter by payment of fees.

Appeal

Any party may appeal from an order by a hearing officer by filing notice of appeal with the FAA Administrator (or a person to whom the Administrator has delegated his/her authority in the matter concerned) within 20 days after issuance of the order. Unless the Administrator expressly provides, the filing of notice of appeal does not stay the effectiveness of the order of immediate compliance. If a notice of appeal is not filed within the required time, the order becomes final.

The person filing the notice of appeal then has a certain period of time to file an appeal brief, stating the reasons why the order should not have been issued. A reply brief is then required to be filed by the opposing party. The Administrator reviews the record and appeal briefs and then issues an order dismissing, reversing, modifying, or affirming the order.

Court Appeals

The decision of the Administrator is final on the part of the FAA and it is precluded from appealing the decisions to courts. In some cases, other parties may appeal to the federal district courts in the judicial district in which the final order was made. A state court has no jurisdiction over the actions of the

FAA Administrator, but the person involved may also be subject to state action if a state law or regulation is also violated.

The appeal to a federal district court must be based on the contention that the action by the FAA official was unreasonable, arbitrary, or contrary to law. In addition, the person must show that he/she has exhausted the right of administrative appeal to the FAA Administrator.

In one recent case appealed to a federal district court, the pilot was unsuccessful since he could not establish that the decision of the hearing officer was arbitrary. In this case, the pilot held a commercial rating and was endorsed for multi-engine rating by an instructor, but never took the flight test. The first time he was scheduled to take the exam, the inspector was unavailable. The second time, the weather was bad and the third time, the pilot did not show. Nevertheless, the pilot checked out a multi-engine aircraft for a flight from Chicago to Florida. On the return trip, the plane iced up and crashed. His license was suspended at the hearing. He appealed to the Administrator on the grounds that he was qualified to fly the airplane and that the issuance of the rating was a mere formality. The federal court refused to cancel the suspension order and held that the pilot had failed to establish that the actions of the FAA were arbitrary.

The federal court will uphold the decision of FAA even though it might have arrived at a different holding based on the same facts as long as there is a reasonable basis for the examiner's decision.

Criminal Actions

In addition to the administrative actions of suspending or revoking a certificate, etc., the FAA may request that either the Attorney General's Office or the local U.S. Attorney take criminal actions against the persons involved.

Here is a sample Notice of Investigation letter:

July 7, 19XX

Certified Mail—Return Receipt Requested

Mr. John Smith
7573 West Avenue
Houston, Texas 77409

Dear Mr. Smith,

Personnel of this office are investigating an incident occurring on July 4, 19XX, which involved the operation of Cessna aircraft N577856 in the vicinity of City Park at approximately 3:30 P.M.

Numerous witnesses have reported that they observed and identified Cessna N577856 diving on picknickers and bathers from 3:30 to 3:45 P.M. A witness informed us that he observed N577856 piloted by you land at the county airport at 3:50 P.M. Operation of this type is contrary to section 91.79(b) of the Federal Aviation Regulations and a menace to public safety.

It appears that the above conditions may be violations of the above cited Federal Aviation Regulation, and we would appreciate receiving any evidence or statements you might wish to make in your behalf within ten days of the receipt of this letter. Any discussion or written statements furnished by you will be given consideration in our investigation. Should our investigation substantiate that a violation did in fact occur, you will be informed of contemplated further action after our investigation is completed.

Sincerely yours,

John L. Doe
Supervisory Inspector

Chapter 8

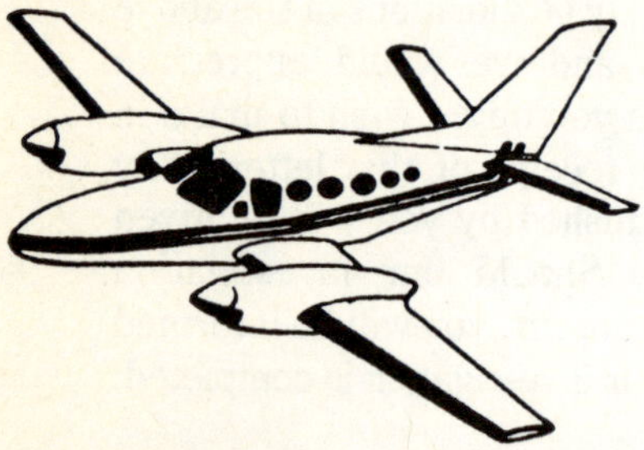

Aviation Insurance

Insurance, an absolute requirement, represents a considerable item of expense to the pilot, owner, FBO, etc. Accordingly, the pilot, etc., should ascertain that he/she has the proper amount and type of insurance. The two basic types of airplane insurance are *hull* and *liability*. Hull covers damage to your airplane, while liability protects you from claims for injuries to others and/or damages to their property.

A key item to remember in buying insurance is that insurance is a specialized type of contract between the insurer (company) and the insuree (person who is being insured).

HULL INSURANCE

Hull insurance may be written to cover any combinations of the below listed hazards:

- ☐ Damages incurred during flight.
- ☐ Damages incurred during taxiing.
- ☐ Fire, theft, hail, wind, and lightning.
- ☐ Hanger or tiedown damage.

The broader the coverage of the insurance policy, the higher the cost. The owner should consider this factor when determining the extent of his/her policy coverage. Hull insurance is normally written with a $500 or $250 deduction.

Some are written with a percentage factor, i.e. the deductible is 5 or 10 percent of the loss. The higher the loss deduction, the cheaper the insurance will be since the pilot, etc., is really self-insuring a portion of the coverage.

Many aircraft owners do not carry hull insurance, thereby taking a chance that they will not lose their aircraft. In making this decision, the pilot, owner, etc., should consider the value of his/her aircraft and his/her ability to replace or repair the airplane. Note: Liability coverage is a *must.*

If the airplane has a mortgage or is subject to a conditional sales contract, normally the party who finances the airplane (bank) will require that the aircraft be covered by hull insurance. In addition, most of the finance contracts require that the party who finances the airplane be named as a party to the insurance policy. This ensures that if the airplane is destroyed, the amount of the debt still unpaid will be paid out of the proceeds of the policy. this requirement protects the lender's investment, therefore making an airplane loan safer and easier to obtain.

If the airplane is equipped with expensive radios and navigation equipment, the hull policy should be examined to ensure coverage of those items.

In the case of damage or loss to the airplane, the insurance policy will pay only for the actual damage or loss not to exceed the face value of the policy. Accordingly, overinsuring the airplane is a waste of money.

If the hull policy covers only in-flight or only ground accidents, then the question often arises whether the accident occurred on the ground or in flight. The general rule is that the accident occurred in flight if it happened from the time the takeoff roll started until the landing roll ended; otherwise, it's a ground accident.

LIABILITY INSURANCE

Liability insurance, like hull insurance, is written in several combinations of coverage. The basic variations of coverage are:

- ☐ Bodily injury liability excluding passengers and the pilot.
- ☐ Bodily injury including coverage for passengers.
- ☐ Medical payments.
- ☐ Property damage.

The normal liability policy includes one or more of the above coverages. In addition, the policy may be written to provide coverage only when the named pilot is operating the aircraft, or it may be extended to include only licensed pilots (i.e., no student pilots), or any person.

The cost of the liability policy is determined by the type and extent of coverage, the experience and past flying record of the pilot, and type of aircraft. Unquestionably, liability insurance is expensive, but an owner/pilot is taking a serious risk when flying without coverage. The owner of a small used airplane may find it cost-effective to fly with liability coverage but not hull insurance.

The amount and type of coverage will vary with each particular situation. For example, if you make it a rule never to allow anyone else to fly your aircraft, then you need coverage only when you are operating the airplane (named pilot coverage only).

The monetary amount of coverage should receive special consideration, since the insuree (person insured) may be responsible for any damages in excess of the policy limits. In addition, many states have insurance regulations that require the operator or owner of an aircraft to carry a minimum amount of liability coverage.

Except in a few states, the injured person does not use the insurance company to collect on the policy, but instead sues the negligent person. Thus, when a pilot is involved in a suit for damages or injuries, the injured person sues the pilot. The pilot's insurance company will then defend the pilot, and in the event that the pilot is held responsible, the insurance company will pay the damages. This occurs when the insurance policy covers the accident. Note later in this chapter the discussion on policy coverage. Less than two percent of all insurance claims are litigated in court. The majority are settled out of court.

If the insurance policy covers the accident, the insurance company has the duty to defend you to the best of their ability. If they fail to do so and the amount awarded is in excess of the policy limits, or if the company had a reasonable opportunity to settle within policy limits and does not do so, the insurance company may be liable for the entire award based on the concept of "bad faith."

Non-Owner's Liability Insurance

The non-owner's liability insurance is designed for the pilot who rents or leases an aircraft. While the airplane owner or the flying service may have liability coverage on the airplane, it is for *their* protection. Thus, if while flying a rented airplane, you are involved in an accident, the owner's policy may or may not cover you. In addition, you may be liable to the owner for loss of the airplane.

Liability insurance is a personal protection for the holder of the policy. Most aviation insurance companies offer a non-owner's policy for renter pilots at reasonable rates. These policies cover the holder when he/she is flying as a pilot, crew member, or passenger of an aircraft having an unrestricted Airworthiness Certificate. This coverage includes the holder when he/she is a passenger on a commercial aircraft, but not for military operations.

The standard non-owner policy will also cover any damage to the aircraft that the policy holder is operating if his/her negligence caused the damage or injury and the policy holder (pilot) does not own any interest in the airplane.

Disclaimers of Liability

The standard liability insurance policies have certain clauses that limit the coverage of the policy in certain circumstances. The most common limitations are:

- ☐ If aircraft is operated in violation of the terms of the pilot's certificate.
- ☐ If aircraft is operated in violation of any Federal Aviation Regulations applicable to aerobatic flying, repairs, maintenances, alterations, inspections, night flying, instrument flying, minimum safe altitude, and while engaged in student instruction.
- ☐ If aircraft is operated in violation of any government regulation or federal or state law.

Note that the language of the above exclusions are so broad as to almost exclude any situation in which an accident occurs. Two questions usually are present in any case involving the effectiveness of these exclusionary clauses. First, is the clause contrary to public policy, and second, if the exclusion was not a casuation factor in the injury or damage, does the clause still exclude coverage?

Courts generally hold that exclusionary clauses are not contrary to public policy. If there is any ambiguity, however, the courts tend to resolve the issue in favor of coverage under the policy.

Most courts have held that the insurance company is not liable if the accident occurs when the aircraft is being operated in violation of an exclusionary clause even if the accident was not caused by the violation referred to in the exclusionary clause. Thus, the general rule is that no causal connection need be shown between the excluded risk and the loss.

In one case, a pilot was involved in an aircraft accident while operating an aircraft without a valid Medical Certificate. The lack of required Medical Certificate had no bearing on the accident. Two days after the accident, the pilot obtained his Medical Certificate. The court, in denying insurance coverage, stated that insurance is a contract between the pilot and the company and that prior to the insurance company being required to pay under the terms of the contract, the pilot must establish coverage. In this case, it was clear that the policy required that the pilot possess a current and valid Medical Certificate at the time of the flight. The fact that the pilot was in good health did not comply fully with the requirement that he *possess* the required certificate.

Illegal Use of the Aircraft

Most policies exclude coverage when the aircraft is being operated in violation of state or federal law. The exclusion was used to exclude coverage for an airplane accident when it was discovered that the airplane involved in the accident contained over 500 kilos of marijuana at the time of the crash. In this case, it appeared that the illegal activity had no bearing on the accident, but coverage was still denied.

Duty to Defend

The general rule as to the duty of the insurance company to defend an action brought against the insured is that if there is a substantial possibility of coverage under the insurance policy, then the insurance company has a duty to defend. Failure to do so constitutes a breach of the insurance contract.

IN CASE OF AN ACCIDENT

Since insurance is a contract between the insurance company and the insured, there are certain steps that an insured should take if involved in any situation where there is a possibility of insurance coverage. First and foremost is the prompt notification of the insurance company. The notice should include the time, place, and circumstances of the incident in question. The notice should also include the names and addresses of witnesses and injured persons.

Other duties of the insured will be listed in the insurance policy. Normally, the policy requires the below listed duties:

- ☐ Cooperate with and assist the insurance company in matters concerning a claim or suit under the policy.
- ☐ Forward promptly all legal papers received.
- ☐ Provide authorization to the insurance company to obtain medical records.
- ☐ Admit no obligation or responsibility nor make any payment other than for first aid to others.
- ☐ Take reasonable steps after an accident to protect the airplane.
- ☐ Allow the insurance company to inspect the airplane before repair or disposal.
- ☐ Report any theft or vandalism to the police promptly.

RELEASE OF LIABILITY AGREEMENTS

Under the provisions of the standard insurance policy, the insurance company has a right when it pays for damages or injuries to sue anyone that the policy holder could sue. Therefore, it is important that the policy holder sign no releases of damages or injuries to anyone without first obtaining approval from the insurance company. This rule is applicable to both liability and hull insurance policies.

SELECTING AN INSURANCE COMPANY

There is an old saying that the best way to find out if your insurance policy is good is to have an accident. Careful consideration in selecting the insurance company and the type of policy coverage, however, before an accident is the preferred method. There are many factors that determine the company you should choose. Since most reliable aviation insurance companies have the same basic combinations of coverage, other factors should also be used. Listed below are some of the more important factors to consider:

1. Is the insurance company an established and reliable company? Great weight should be placed on this consideration, as the policy is only as good as the company that issued it.

2. Is the company licensed to do business within your state? A company may sell by mail order and yet not be licensed to conduct business within the state. Thus, a non-licensed insurance company would not be subject to state regulation by the insurance commission of your state. As these commissions exist to protect the consumers, this is one added protection that a person should have.

3. What type of claim service does the company have? Rapid reimbursement or replacement of the aircraft will lessen the hardship connected with any accident.

4. Ensure that the company does not include in their policy an exclusion clause for accidents occurring in violation of the Federal Aviation Regulations. Another method of stating this exclusion is to include the following type of statement in their policy: "This policy does not apply under IFR conditions unless the pilot possesses a valid instrument ticket and is proceeding in accordance with instrument flight rules." The problem with these exclusions is that if you suddenly find yourself in IFR conditions with no valid instrument ticket, then you are uninsured at the time you most need insurance.

A similar clause to avoid in one which provides that coverage of the policy applies only when the aircraft is flown by a pilot properly certified for the aircraft and the flight conditions involved.

5. Does the policy have an unearned premium clause? In other words, what happens to the remaining insurance premiums if the aircraft is totally destroyed before the end of the policy year (date policy expires)? Are you still required to pay the entire year's premiums? This situation may never happen to you, but if it does, you should understand in advance what your position will be.

6. Does your insurance policy cover you when you rent or borrow an airplane? Many policies are written to cover the policy holder only when he/she is operating an aircraft of the same type and seating capacity as the pilot owns. This may be all the coverage that a person needs, but beware of the restriction and of the fact that when you are flying a different type of aircraft, you may not be covered.

LIFE INSURANCE

The majority of life insurance companies require a pilot to pay an added premium or they include an aviation exclusion clause in the policy. However, once the policy is written, the company cannot change it and add the exclusion. Accordingly, if you are not a pilot but intend to start taking lessons soon, review your life insurance coverage first. Any additional coverage purchased after a person has started taking flying lessons could be subject to this exclusion clause or the added premiums.

An aviation exclusion clause is one that provides that if the insured (pilot) is killed in an aviation accident when the insured was either a pilot or crew member, the only amount due under the policy will be the amount of premiums paid in, plus interest. The insurance policy must expressly state that the insured is subject to the aviation exclusion clause or the courts will require full payment of the policy.

Some pilots in order to avoid the exclusion clause have failed to reveal the fact of prior aviation experience when applying for life insurance. The courts uniformly refuse to allow recovery on the policy if the pilot concealed the information of prior aviation experience if the death is caused by an aviation related accident.

In a Florida case, the deceased gave a negative answer to a question as to whether he had made any aerial flights in the last five years as a pilot or crew member. Actually, he had accumulated 36 hours of flight time several years previously. He was killed in an aircraft accident during military flight training and his family was not allowed to recover on the policy because of the misstatement of facts. Therefore, to be safe, when buying life insurance, inform the agent or company of any prior aviation experience you may have.

Some insurance companies have always given the experienced aviator a reduction of the added premiums when he/she has accumulated over 400 hours of flight time. Some leading life insurance companies recently have started writing life policies to aviators without the flight restriction or added premiums. This change is attributed to recent improvements in aviation safety.

It is hoped that this trend becomes widespread in the insurance industry. Until it does, shop around to find a reliable company that will issue to the pilot a policy without the added premium or exclusion clause. In this regard, I have had several experienced life insurance agents wrongly assure me that all life insurance companies have the same types of aviation exclusion clauses and premium rates for aviators.

Chapter 9

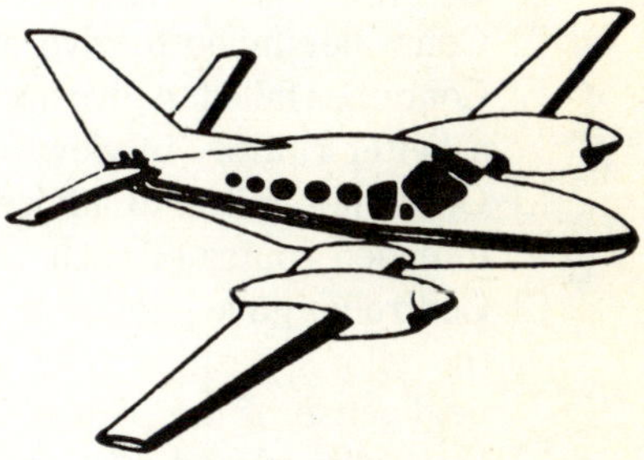

Control of Airspace

U.S. Code 49, section 1305, states that there is a recognized, and declared to exist in behalf of any citizen of the United States, a public right of freedom of transit through the navigable airspace of the United States.

The FARs state that the primary objective of the Air Traffic Control Service shall be to promote the safe, orderly, and expeditious movement of air traffic.

As noted in Chapter 6, the federal government may be liable for negligent acts by government employees acting in the scope of their employment under the Federal Tort Claims Act. A question when discussing negligence of air traffic controllers is whether or not the "discretionary function" exception excludes coverage of air traffic controllers. Most courts that have examined this question have held that the types of activities involved on the part of air traffic controllers is not the type of "discretionary function" excluded from liability by the tort claims act. Accordingly, the government has been held liable for the negligence of air traffic controllers. Note: In most cases, the claim is against the government with no right to proceed against the air traffic controllers personally.

Some of the cases in which the government has been held liable for the negligence for air traffic controllers include:

- ☐ Air traffic controller issued a wake turbulence warning and then take-off clearance to a Piper Cub piloted by a student pilot.

- ☐ Air traffic controller failed to warn pilot of Piper as to wake turbulence reported by other aircraft.
- ☐ Controller misstated the Minimum Descent Altitude.
- ☐ Controller failed to advise aircraft that it was perilous left of course.
- ☐ Controller assigned a pattern altitude of 800 foot downwind when there was a 819 foot radio tower within two miles of the airport, and did not give aircraft warning of the existence of tower.
- ☐ Controller gave improper altimeter setting.
- ☐ Controller failed to give priority to aircraft with engine trouble.
- ☐ Controller failed to give accurate weather data and failed to recommend a better runway in view of deteriorating weather conditions.
- ☐ Controller failed to advise two taxiing aircraft of the positions and intended routes of each.
- ☐ Controller gave pilot clearance to "cruise 4,000" without determining the pilot's position over mountainous terrain. (Note: Contributory negligence of the pilot prevented the pilot from recovering.)
- ☐ Controller placed a DC-9 and a Cessna 150 on a collision course and failed to warn either aircraft.
- ☐ Controller directed a pilot flying IFR into an area of potential thunderstorms rather than a safer route.

There was told to be no liability in the following cases:

- ☐ Failure to give additional warning of wake turbulence to an experienced pilot.
- ☐ Failure to advise pilot in VFR weather of necessity to maintain altitude. Court stated that under VFR conditions, it is the pilot, not the tower personnel, who is responsible for the selection and maintenance of altitude, separation, and course.
- ☐ Providing only 1,000 feet of vertical separation between aircraft.
- ☐ Providing erroneous altimeter setting where evidence indicates that the incorrect altimeter setting was not the proximate cause of the accident.
- ☐ It was not negligent for the controller to fail to observe and warn a jet aircraft attempting to take off on an inactive runway where four aircraft were parked.

There is a general rule that the pilot, not the air controller, has the primary responsibility—at least in VFR weather—to avoid collisions.

Chapter 10

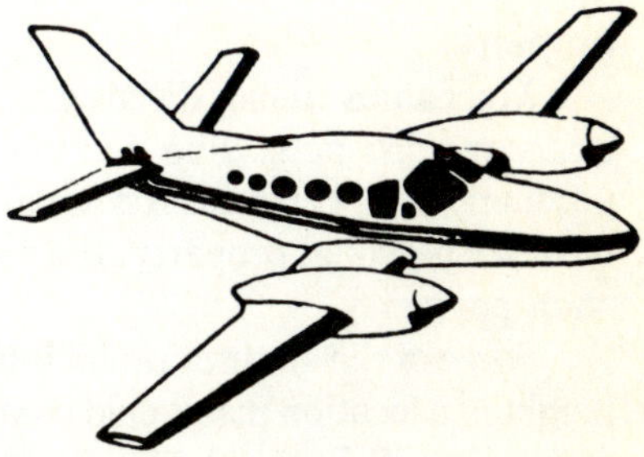

State Regulations and Licensing Requirements

Federal statutes (49 U.S. Code 1305) provide that no state or political subdivision thereof and no interstate agency or political agency shall enact or enforce any law, rule, regulation, standard, etc., relating to the rates, routes, or services of any air carrier operating under federal regulations to provide air transportation. The exception to this is for air transportation by an intrastate carrier (wholly within the state) regulated by a state on or prior to August 1, 1977.

Courts have held that the following situations cannot be controlled by state regulations or statutes, since they are preempted by federal law:

- ☐ California statutes do not apply to a blind passenger's claim for damages arising from the airline's insisting that the passenger sit in the front row of the passenger section of the aircraft.
- ☐ The city of Clearwater, Texas could not restrict passenger airlines from landing after certain hours at the local airport when permitted by federal regulations.

STATE AERONAUTICS ACTS

Most states have state aeronautics acts to regulate those aspects of aviation that are left to state control and to supplement the federal regulations. If there is a conflict with the state act and the federal regulation, in most cases, the federal rules will prevail.

The most common state acts provide for the financing and control of local airports and air navigation facilities. In addition, they normally provide the state with condemnation authority so that the state may condemn private property for the purposes of buying the property for use as an airport. This public taking is under the concept that there is a greater public necessity for the property.

Mechanics' liens, discussed in Chapter 4, are also provided for in most state aviation acts. The lien clause generally provides that, to enforce the payment of any charges for repairs, improvements, storage, or care of aircraft or other personal property, the airport operator has a lien on the property for such payment.

Some of the statutes prohibit building of structures in excess of a prescribed height in a location that would create a hazardous condition for airplanes landing or taking off. Some also prohibit the construction of public utility poles and lines in a manner that constitutes a hazard to air navigation.

Most states require prior approval of airport sites before the construction or establishment of an airport. The authority to approve or disapprove is normally vested in the state Department of Aviation. In addition, in most states, the Department of Aviation may revoke any airport permit if it determines that there has been an abandonment of the site or airport, a failure to develop the airport, the airport no longer conforms to minimum standards, the operator or owner has failed to comply with any rule or regulation of the department, or the site may no longer be safely used as an airport. Prior to the revocation of a permit or the failure to issue one, the persons concerned are provided a right to an administrative hearing. The rules and procedures for administrative hearings are similar to those employed by National Transportation Safety Board and the FAA, as discussed in Chapter 7.

Subject to the restrictions imposed by federal regulations, the state Department of Aviation may adopt and enforce noise standards governing the operation of aircraft and aircraft engines in vicinity of airports.

STATE FINANCIAL RESPONSIBILITY ACTS

Most states have enacted state financial responsibility acts which require aircraft owners and operators to have either insurance (liability) or other security to establish the ability to pay any damages that may be assessed against the owner or operator as the result of an accident. (Also note discussion of liability requirements contained in Chapter 8.)

The acts also require in most cases that accidents be reported to the state Department of Aviation. This reporting requirement is in addition to the FAR reporting requirements. For example, the State of California requires the reporting of all aviation accidents that occurred within the state if any person is killed or injured or there is damage in excess of $400 to property of any person other than the property owned by the owner or operator of the airplane. The report must be made within 48 hours of the accident to the chief of police or sheriff of the county in which the accident occurred. If the owner or operator dies as the results of the accident, the legal representative must report this fact to the state Department of Aviation within 15 days in addition to the immediate report required to the chief of police or sheriff.

A common requirement is that any aircraft owner or leasor must inform in writing anyone who rents their aircraft as to the status of liability insurance on the aircraft. Under the jurisdictional aspects of the acts, the operation of an aircraft within the state is considered sufficient to allow service of court process on the operator. This aspect of the act is very similar to the "long-arm" statutes that permit a person to sue an out-of-state automobile driver in the state based on an incident arising out of the driving.

The state aircraft financial responsibility acts do not normally apply to:

- ☐ Military aircraft or aircraft owned by the U.S. or a foreign government.
- ☐ Aircraft under the sole control of any state or political subdivision of a state (city, county, etc.).
- ☐ Scheduled commercial air carriers.

Chapter 11

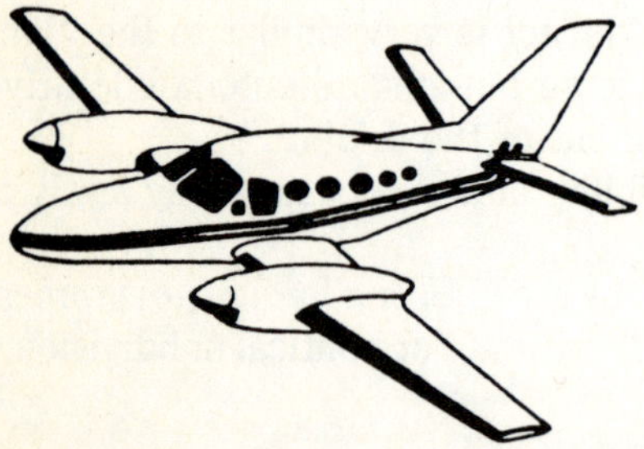

The Fixed Based Operator

In this chapter, the standard of care and other liability problems of fixed based operators (FBOs) will be discussed. FBOs should also note the discussions contained in Chapter 6 regarding negligence and personal liability, Chapter 7 regarding aircraft accidents and investigations, and Chapter 8 regarding aviation insurance problems.

STANDARD OF CARE

The courts have uniformly held that an airport operator has the duty to exercise ordinary care to keep the premises in a reasonably safe condition. The general rules of negligence apply. This means that an airport operator is held to the standard of a reasonably prudent person in performing the duties of an airport operator. If the actions of the FBO are of the type that a careful person would apply, then, in most cases, there is no negligence.

Some of the cases which have looked at the liability of fixed base operators are listed below:

The operator of an airplane tiedown area was held liable for damage to an aircraft based on the theory that the operator failed to provide a good quality tiedown rope. In a similar case, judgment in favor of the aircraft owner was approved on appeal where the rope furnished by the FBO was defective. Note: To avoid this problem, many operators require the airplane owners to furnish their own rope.

Owners or operators of airports have been held liable for the failure to either mark high-tension power and telephone lines in the vicinity of the airport, or to warn pilots of this hazard.

In one case, an operator of a private airstrip was not held responsible for the crash of an airplane where the pilot was also negligent in making a straight approach to the airport and was flying below the tops of the clearly visible transmission lines. The court determined that had the pilot followed correct procedures, he would have noticed the transmission lines.

In another case, the operator of a private airstrip marked the airport with large Xs to indicate that the airport was closed. The pilot crashed while attempting to land on the strip. The crash was the result of unmarked telephone wires. The court held that since the airport was closed to the public, the pilot assumed the risk of injury when he landed.

One airport operator was held liable when it was established that he had full custody, care, and control of aircraft and was negligent in allowing automobile traffic to traverse the concrete apron near and around the tiedown area. The operator was liable when an unidentified automobile hit the parked aircraft.

The fixed-base operator was not liable for damage to an aircraft at a private field when the airplane, while attempting to taxi through grass from the runway to the designated tiedown area, tipped over nose-first when the nose wheel dropped into a hole approximately two feet deep. The court found that the FBO did not know of the hole and was not negligent in failing to discover it.

The airport operator was found not liable for the drowning death of a skydiver in a lake near the airport. The court determined that the lake posed an obvious danger to any skydivers and therefore the diver assumed the risk.

A court in one case determined that an employee of the fixed base operator had no duty to stop a pilot under the influence of alcohol from taking off in the pilot's own airplane.

LANDING ADVISORIES

At uncontrolled airports, there is usually no liability for failing to give landing advisories over Unicom. If, however, one is given and it causes an accident, then the operator may be liable to the damage.

LIABILITY FOR CONDITION OF RUNWAYS

On those private airports where the FBO is also under a duty to maintain the runways, there is a duty to either maintain the runways or to warn pilots of the hazards. In one case, for example, the FBO was held liable for rough runways where there was no proper warning of this hazard. The FBO is also under a duty in these cases to exercise reasonable care to keep the runways free of people and automobiles. In one case, this duty was held to include the construction of barricades and warning devices to keep automobiles off the runway.

Failing to properly mark runways and insufficient lighting is considered sufficient to establish negligence on the part of the operator in some cases. In addition, the FBO has a duty to mark utility lines and poles in the taxi area and the failure to do so has resulted in a liability finding against the FBO.

LIABILITY FOR PEDESTRIANS

FBOs are liable for the failure to take the necessary steps to warn pedestrians of the potential dangers that exist at the airport. A boy riding his bicycle was hit and killed by an airplane attempting to land. The FBO was held liable for failure to warn pedestrians or bicycle riders of the dangers involved.

BAILMENT

When a transient airplane is parked at the FBO's area, is the FBO liable for damage to the aircraft? (Note the above cases on defective tiedown ropes.) The answer to this question depends on whether or not the FBO merely rents a space to park the aircraft or takes possession of the aircraft. If the FBO takes possession of the aircraft, then the FBO has a duty to use reasonable care to protect the aircraft. If the FBO merely rents a space, his/her liability is substantially less.

SNOW AND ICE

If the FBO also has the duty to maintain the runways, there is a duty to take reasonable care to maintain the runways free of snow and ice. Note: This does not mean that the FBO is liable in all cases where the runways are iced over or covered in snow, only that the FBO has a duty to use reasonable care. The FBO also appears to have a reasonable time to clear the runways after a snowfall.

AGREEMENTS TO LIMIT LIABILITY

Agreements to limit liability on the part of FBOs are not favored by the courts. Agreements to limit an FBO from any liability is, in most states, in violation of public policy. Most courts will allow a reasonable agreement to restrict the amount of liability recoverable.

SECURITY PROGRAMS

FAR Part 107.3 requires each airport operator to adopt and carry out a security program to provide for the safety of persons and property traveling in air transportation and intrastate (within the state) air transportation against acts of criminal violence and aircraft piracy. The regulation requires that the program be in writing and signed by the airport operator or any person to whom the airport operator has delegated this authority.

Chapter 12

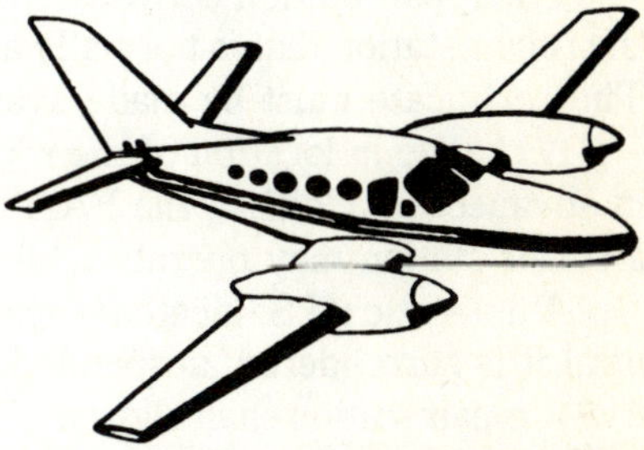

Services and Repair

In this chapter, the requirements and legal responsibilities of repair stations and mechanics will be discussed. As noted earlier, in Chapter 5, the owner or operator of an aircraft is primarily responsible for maintaining that aircraft in an airworthy condition. In most cases, however, the owner or operator is not qualified to perform the necessary inspections or mechanical work on the aircraft.

The courts have held mechanics and repair stations liable for the negligent inspection or repair of aircraft. This liability extends to other persons who are injured or suffer damage because of the failure to discover a potential safety problem during an inspection, or the negligent repair of an aircraft. Note: In order to find the mechanic or repair station liable, the negligence must be the proximate cause of the accident.

In one case, a court held a mechanic liable for his negligence in overhauling an engine that failed in flight two years later. It appeared that the mechanic used substandard parts and this was the cause of the engine failure and the resulting accident. In a similar case, an AI was held liable for the failure to discover a latent defect in the aircraft control systems that failed and caused an accident.

REPAIR STATIONS

FAR Part 145 contains the regulations on repair stations. The basic regulations generally provide that no one may operate a certified repair station or advertise as operating a certified repair station until a certificate has been issued.

An application for a repair station certificate is made to the FAA Administrator on the required form and submitted with duplicate copies of the station's inspection procedures manual and a list of maintenance functions to be performed by the station. A physical description of the facilities (with photographs) and an organizational chart that includes the names and titles of managing and supervisory personnel should also be included.

The repair station certificate and ratings must be displayed at a place in the repair station that is normally accessible to the public and is not obscured. The certificate must be made available for inspection by the FAA.

A change in location of the repair station must be approved by the FAA in advance. In addition, the FAA may prescribe the conditions under which a repair station may operate while it is changing its location.

A domestic (U.S.-located) repair station's certificate or rating is effective until it is surrendered, suspended, or revoked.

A repair station shall allow an FAA representative to inspect it at any time to determine its compliance with the FARs. The inspections may cover the adequacy of the repair station's inspection system, records, and its general ability to comply with the FARs. After any FAA inspection, the repair station will be notified in writing of any defects found during the inspection.

When a certified repair station indicates in advertising that it is a certified repair station, it must clearly state its certificate number. This requirement applies to letterhead stationery, billheads and statements, hangar or shop signs, magazine advertising, or any form of promotional media.

In the application for approval of a certified repair station, at least one person must be designated as a repairman. Each person recommended as a repairman must be at or above the level of shop foreman or department head or be responsible for supervising the work performed by the repair station. The person signing the application must certify to the FAA Administrator that the person or persons recommended as repairmen are able to perform and supervise the assigned work of the station.

The repair station must maintain a roster of its supervisory personnel, including the names of the officials of the station that are responsible for its management and the names of its technical supervisors, such as foreman and crew chiefs. A roster of its inspection personnel, including the names of the chief inspector and those inspectors who make final airworthiness determinations before releasing an article to service, is also required.

The repair station shall provide a summary of the employment of each person whose name is on one of the above noted rosters. The summary shall contain enough information as to each person to establish compliance with the experience requirements of the FARs. This information includes:

- ☐ Present position and title.
- ☐ Total years of experience in the type of work the person is doing.

- ☐ Past employment record, with names of places and terms of employment by month and year.
- ☐ Scope of present employment (e.g., airframe overhaul, airframe final assembly, etc.).
- ☐ The type and number of the mechanic or repairman certificate or rating that each person holds.

Rosters should be updated to reflect the termination of any employees or any appreciable changes in the duties of each person. The rosters and summaries must be made available for inspection by an FAA designee at any time.

Each repair station shall maintain adequate records of all work that it does, naming the certificated mechanic or repairman who performed or supervised the work, and the inspector of that work. The records must be kept for at least two years after the work it applies to is done.

Each station shall report to the FAA within 72 hours after it discovers any serious defect in or other recurring unairworthy condition of an airplane, powerplant, propeller, or any component of any of them.

LEGAL LIABILITY FOR NEGLIGENCE

Mechanics and repair stations are liable for the negligent repair of airplanes or component parts of airplanes, if that negligence is the proximate cause of the injuries or damages. In addition, if the mechanic observes a dangerous condition while working on an airplane, the mechanic has a duty to warn of this condition to the aircraft owner or pilot unless it is obvious that the owner/pilot is aware of the condition.

In some cases, the courts have held that there is an implied warranty that the mechanic or repair station will use a high standard of care in repairing airplanes. This means that the mechanic is liable for failure to exercise reasonable care in the repair of an airplane.

Some of the court cases that have examined the liability of mechanics and repair stations include:

- ☐ Mechanic was not liable where engine operated 325 hours after repair and before failure, since there was no evidence that the mechanical work was improperly done.
- ☐ Mechanic was held liable for engine repair where contaminated oil was used in the engine by the mechanic after the repair.
- ☐ Repair station was held liable for taxiing accident with a parked airplane when it was established that the mechanic, in repairing the hydraulic system, had failed to refill the system.

Chapter 13

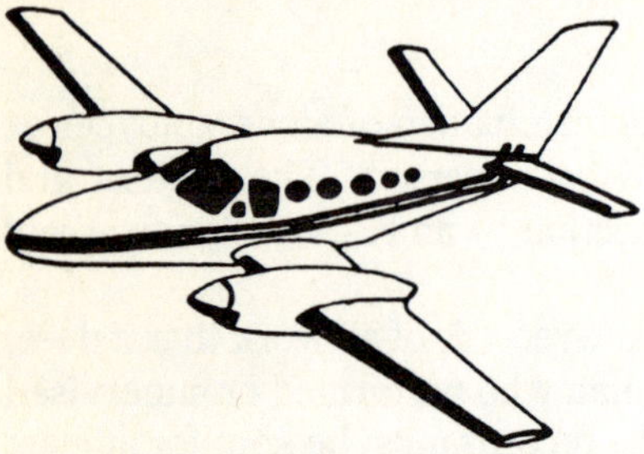

Homebuilts and Ultralights

The first successful homebuilt was built in Dayton, Ohio, and then transported to Kitty Hawk, North Carolina, for its first flight on December 17, 1903, by Orville Wright. From that first airplane, the homebuilt movement has grown to the extent that in 1986, it was estimated that there were at least 22,000 homebuilt aircraft under construction or completed.

EXPERIMENTAL AIRCRAFT LIMITATIONS

FAR Part 91.42 provides that no person may operate an aircraft with an Experimental Certificate for purposes other than the purpose for which the certificate was issued or carry persons or property for compensation or hire.

That FAR also provides that an Experimental aircraft may not be operated outside an assigned area until it is shown that:

- ☐ The aircraft is controllable throughout its normal range of speeds and throughout all the maneuvers to be executed.
- ☐ The aircraft has no hazardous operating characteristics or design features.

Unless authorized by FAA in special limitations, no person may operate an Experimental aircraft over a densely populated area or in a congested airway. Any special limitations issued in this regard may contain additional terms and conditions necessary in the interest of the safety of air commerce.

Each person operating on an Experimental Certificate shall:

- ☐ Advise each passenger of the experimental nature of the aircraft.
- ☐ Operate only under VFR (Visual Flight Rules), day only, unless special authorization otherwise is obtained from FAA.
- ☐ Notify the control tower of the experimental nature of the aircraft when operating the aircraft into or out of airports with operating control towers.

The FAA may prescribe additional limitations that are considered necessary, including limitations on the persons who may be carried on the aircraft.

STANDARDS OF CARE

In general, the operator of an Experimental aircraft has the same liability responsibilities as operators of other aircraft to third persons. In addition, there may be a higher standard of care required of passengers who are not familiar with the nature of the aircraft.

As noted earlier, there is a requirement to notify passengers of the experimental nature of the aircraft. If the passengers are not knowledgeable in aviation, special care should be exercised to ensure that they understand completely that the aircraft is homebuilt and of an experimental nature.

The builder of a homebuilt has been held liable in some cases for the negligent construction of the aircraft. In one case, the builder deviated from the tested plans in building the aircraft. He then sold the aircraft to another pilot without informing the pilot of the change. As a direct result of the change, there was a structural failure during a hard landing, causing injury to the pilot. The pilot was allowed to recover from the builder.

PAPERWORK

Before 1985, the aircraft builder would notify the FAA that he was building an aircraft and have the primary structure inspected before it was covered or otherwise became inaccessible. A final inspection would be required, and then FAA would assign a flight test area for the test period of 25 hours (if the engine and propeller were Type Certificated) or 40 hours (all other cases).

The certification policy was changed by Advisory Circular 20-27C (AC 20-27C), published by the FAA in 1986. AC 20-27C is reprinted in Appendix III. The essential requirements are listed below:

1. Builder must keep copies of invoices and shipping documents for all materials, kits, tubing, etc. The inspector will also need to see these documents to ensure that only aviation-quality materials have been used in the craft.

2. Builder must keep a construction log to document the construction and inspection of the airplane during construction phase. All records of

inspections should be included in the log. A logbook designed specifically to meet the FAA requirements set forth in AC 20-27C may be obtained from: Aerorecords 6854 Antiqua Way, Sacramento CA 95831.

3. Aircraft pre-cover inspections required may now be done by any knowledgeable person (recommend at least a certified mechanic).

4. After the airplane is completed, the builder should present the documents to the inspector at the time the aircraft is inspected by the FAA inspector. If the aircraft passes inspection, a limited Airworthiness Certificate is issued.

5. Test flights must be documented as to length, type, handling of the aircraft, cooling, etc. Any problems noted should be logged, along with entries noting that the corrections have been made. The final flight test should indicate that the airplane is controllable throughout its normal range of CG and airspeeds. Any aerobatic maneuvers performed during test period should also be logged.

6. On the completion of the test period, 25 or 40 hours, the builder presents aircraft documents to the FAA for an unlimited Airworthiness Certificate. If the paperwork is in order, the FAA may issue the certificate without any additional inspections of the aircraft.

Since 1979, Experimental Certificates for homebuilt aircraft have an unlimited duration. FAA inspectors still perform the original certification, as noted above, prior to first flight. Each builder may obtain FAA certification as a "repairman" and be thus approved to perform airplane condition inspections. To be certified as a "repairman," the builder must apply at the time of the original certification of the aircraft.

INSURANCE

For the general principles of aviation insurance, see Chapter 9. Liability insurance is a necessity for any aircraft owner, including the owner of a homebuilt or ultralight. A person flying without at least liability insurance is risking everything he owns and more. In addition, most builders have invested a substantial amount of time and money in their airplanes. Accordingly, hull insurance should be considered.

Most insurance companies will not insure homebuilts. One company, AVEMCO (7315 Wisconsin Avenue, Bethesda, MD 20014) actively seeks the homebuilt insurance business. The Experimental Aircraft Association (EAA) also provides a insurance program for its members.

One of the Avemco Company's standard policies includes reimbursement at $5 per hour for the time invested in rebuilding the airplane if it is destroyed.

Since insurance is essential, this is one of the factors that a potential homebuilder should consider before selecting the model to build. Check with other builders of the same model being considered as to any problems they may have experienced in obtaining insurance. My experience is that the average aviation insurance agent does not understand homebuilts. Find an agent or company that specializes or does a substantial business in homebuilts.

KIT PLANES

Many legal problems have been created by the purchasing of kits to build homebuilts and ultralights. There are some on the market that are unsafe and best ignored. An experienced builder lists the below suggestions for purchasing of kits:

1. Buy from only established and proven companies. Check with previous buyers as to the support provided by company, ease of building, etc. Obtain a list of previous buyers from the company and check with several of them regarding the quality of the kits sold.
2. Don't buy the kit piecemeal. Too many buyers have stretched out the buying of the kit only to find the company has gone out of business or no longer makes the component parts needed.
3. Since most of us cannot afford to buy a kit for cash, see your local bank about financing the package.
4. Don't buy a project that is over your head.

ULTRALIGHTS

The ultralight movement is credited to Francis M. Rogallo, a NASA engineer at the Langley Research Center. He developed a flexible-wing paraglider for military applications. Later, Bill Bennett of Australia adopted the device for sport flying by using it in tow behind a speedboat on water skis. Next, Jack Lambie and his sixth-grade class built a 28-foot biplane hang glider for less than $25.00; the 16 year-old son of an aerospace engineer, Taras Kiceniuk, designed the Icarus, a swept-wing, tailless ultralight.

The first engines were added by John Moody of Milwaukee, who added a chainsaw engine to the Icarus II. Less than a decade later, it was estimated that approximately 25,000 ultralights were in existence. The accident rates and fatalities involved with ultralights appear similar to those of the early years of aviation.

In a 1984 study by the NTSB of 177 ultralight accidents, the NTSB concluded that airframe failure was involved in those accidents six times more frequently than in general aviation accidents. The study also noted that most airframe failures occurred in homebuilt ultralights.

Ultralight rules and regulations are contained in Part 103 of the FARs. A summary of those rules is listed below:

1. An ultralight vehicle is defined as a vehicle designed for a single occupant, used for recreation or sport purposes only, has no Airworthiness Certificate, if unpowered weighs less than 155 pounds, if powered weighs less than 254 pounds, and has a fuel capacity of less than five U.S. gallons, maximum airspeed of 55 knots or less in level flight, and a power-off stall speed of 24 knots or less.

2. Inspections required are that the operator must, upon request of an FAA administrator or designee, allow the administrator or designee to inspect the vehicle. In addition, if required, the operator must furnish satisfactory proof that the vehicle is subject to FAR Part 103.

3. Ultralights are not required to meet the Airworthiness Certification standards.

4. Ultralight operators are not required to have Pilot or Medical Certificates, nor the age, experience, or aeronautical requirements necessary for normal aircraft operations.

5. Ultralight vehicles are not required to be marked or registered.

6. No person may operate an ultralight in a hazardous manner.

7. No person may allow an object to be dropped from an ultralight if such action creates a hazard to other persons or property.

8. Ultralights may be operated only between the hours of sunrise and sunset or during the twilight periods of 30 minutes prior to sunrise and 30 minutes after sunset.

9. Ultralights must yield the right-of-way to all aircraft; powered ultralights must yield to unpowered ones.

10. Ultralights may not be operated over congested areas, restricted areas, prohibited areas, nor within an Airport Traffic Area, Control Zone, Terminal Control Area, or any other positive control area without prior authorization.

11. Ultralights may operate only by visual reference with the surface.

12. Ultralights must follow VFR conditions.

Chapter 14

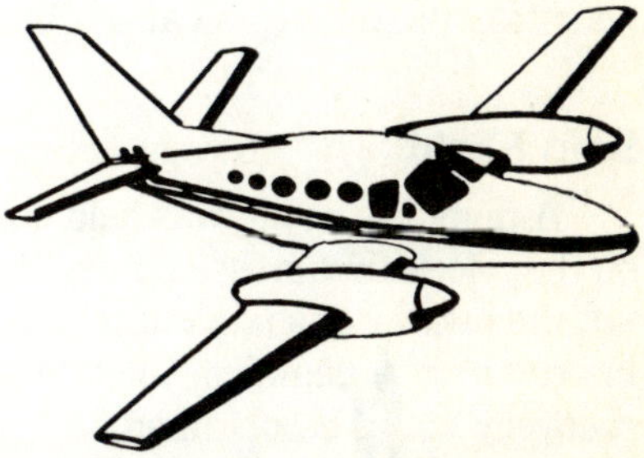

Flight Instruction

In this chapter, the legal aspects of flight instruction will be discussed. The earlier rules and legal concepts involving negligence should also be considered.

LIABILITY

A review of some court cases involving flight instructor liabilities for personal injuries or damages to property is listed below.

Duty to Protect Student

A California court held a flight instructor liable for the injury to a novice flying student when the instructor asked the student to remove the chock from in front of the wheel of a Piper Cub with the engine running. The student was struck by the propeller and suffered major head injuries. The court stated that the flight instructor knew the danger of a rotating propeller, but the student, being new to flying, did not. In addition, the court indicated that the instructor has a duty to protect the student from such known hazards.

Failure to Keep Proper Lookout

In a midair collision, involving a student pilot and an instructor, with another aircraft, the court held that the primary responsibility to keep a proper lookout rests with the instructor, not the student. Accordingly, the student could recover damages against the instructor even though the student was flying the aircraft at the time of the collision.

Criminal Liability

An instructor was held criminally liable for violation of a city ordinance which made it unlawful to leave any aircraft upon a city airport with the engine running unless a licensed pilot, student pilot endorsed for solo flight, or a certified mechanic is in the aircraft. In this case, the instructor left a student pilot who had not been endorsed for solo flight in the aircraft. During this period of time, for some reason the throttle advanced, causing the aircraft to move forward and strike another aircraft. Note: The instructor was also liable in civil court for the damages caused by the accident.

Solo Flight

A flight instructor was held not liable for damage caused by a student pilot on the pilot's first cross-country flight. The court stated that an instructor was not the insurer of a student pilot and that unless it can be established that the instructor was negligent in endorsing the student for cross-country flight, no recovery could be obtained.

In a similar situation, a flying school and the instructor were held not liable for the damages caused by one of the student pilots. In this case, the student pilot negligently collided with the aircraft of the plaintiff while the student was taxiing for takeoff.

Parked Aircraft

An instructor was held liable for damages to a rented aircraft as the result of windstorm. In this case, the instructor and the student of a dual cross-country flight landed at an alternate airport because of an approaching windstorm. The instructor asked the student to tie down the aircraft while he called the home base to inform them that the aircraft had been diverted. The aircraft was improperly tied down by the student.

Improper Inspection

A flight instructor has held liable for approving the flight plan of a relatively inexperienced student pilot. In this case, the pilot was allowed to take off in a heavily loaded airplane, which stalled on takeoff. Inspection of the wreckage indicated that the baggage compartment was overloaded and that the load was not properly distributed.

Duty of Care to Students

One federal court held that flight instructors who give flying lessons have a duty, equal to highest duty a commercial airline owes to its passengers, of care in furnishing instruction to flying students who have not yet soloed.

Turbulent Wake Accident

A flying school and the flight instructor were held liable for the death of a student pilot whose small aircraft crashed while taking off at an airport when the small plane crossed the path of the turbulent wake of a large jet aircraft. In this case, the federal court found that the instructor was negligent in failing to give the student instruction on the dangers of wake turbulence. The flying school was held liable for failing to furnish an instructor fully aware of the dangers of the turbulent wake of large aircraft.

In a similar case, a student was held not liable for damage to his rented light aircraft. The accident was caused by turbulence encountered taking off at an airport when his airplane crossed the path of a large jet aircraft. The court determined that the flight instructor was in charge of the aircraft, not the student. This was the student's second solo flight and the instructor had made a trip around the pattern with the student before turning the aircraft over to the student for solo flight.

In a similar wake turbulence case involving dual flight instruction, the student was allowed to recover from the flight instructor and the flying school where the flight instructor allowed the student to take off immediately after the departure of large commercial jet.

Licensed Pilots

In a case involving the death of an instructor and a licensed Private Pilot receiving dual instruction, a New Mexico court held the instructor's estate not liable where there was no evidence that the instructor was flying the aircraft nor was there any evidence of who was negligent at the time of the accident. In this case, the court noted that both occupants were fully capable of operating the aircraft at the time of the accident.

BREACH OF CONTRACT

Courts have held that the general rules of contract law apply to contracts to provide flight instruction. These rules apply also to those situations where there are no formal or written contracts, since contracts may be intended from the actions of the parties. Included in contractual concepts is the implied warranty that the flight instructor is competent to perform his or her instructional duties.

On breach of contract, the normal court remedy is for recovery of damages.

One problem with applying the contractual rules to flight instruction involves flight instruction for juveniles. A minor may, after reaching majority (age 18 in most states), disaffirm the contract for flight instruction (cancel it) and demand a return on any money paid. Courts have allowed minors to recover the money spent on flight instruction even though they could not return the instruction received. For this reason, and to ensure that the minor's parents approve the minor's flight instruction, always require parents' signatures prior to providing flight instruction to minors. If the parents are separated, make sure that the parent giving permission has the authority to do so. In many cases, the court awards legal custody to only one of the parents and only that parent has the right to consent.

INSURANCE COVERAGE

Most fixed based operators and flying schools have insurance coverage to protect themselves from lawsuits arising out of injuries to persons or damage to property. These policies, while providing protection for the FBO or the flying school, may not protect the flight instructor for losses caused by his or her negligence. The instructor should either obtain his or her own insurance or ensure that the FBO or flying school has a rider on the insurance that also protects the instructor.

FAA REGULATION OF INSTRUCTORS

As provided by federal statute, the Federal Aviation Administrator is empowered to provide for the examination and rating of flight instructors. The guidance is provided by FAR Part 61. That FAR provides generally:

No one may give required flight instruction to qualify a person for solo flight, solo cross-country, or Pilot or Flight Instructor Certificate or rating unless the instructor has a Flight Instructor Certificate issued by the FAA with an appropriate rating on that certificate.

No one may endorse a pilot logbook to show that he or she had given flight instruction or endorse a student pilot certificate or logbook for solo operating privileges unless the instructor is a certified Flight Instructor with appropriate rating on that certificate.

A Flight Instructor Certificate is effective only while the holder has a current Pilot Certificate and a Medical Certificate appropriate to the pilot privileges being exercised.

A Flight Instructor Certificate expires at the end of the 24th month after the month in which it is issued or last renewed.

Any flight instruction received from a flight instructor not certificated by the FAA may not be considered in meeting required instruction unless the instruction is given in a program for training of military pilots or by a flight instructor licensed by a foreign contracting nation and the flight instruction is given outside the United States.

Eligibility

The eligibility for flight instructor certificate is:

1. Be at least 18 years of age;
2. Read, write and converse fluently in English;

3. Aviation qualifications of appropriate Commercial or Airline Transport Pilot Certificate and an instrument rating, if the person is applying for an airplane or an Instrument Instructor rating.

4. Pass a written test on required ground subjects of
   a. the learning process;
   b. elements of effective teaching;
   c. student evaluation, quizzing, and testing;
   d. course development;
   e. lesson planning; and
   f. classroom instructing techniques.

5. Pass an oral and flight test on required aviation subjects of
   a. preparation and conduct of lesson plans for students with varying backgrounds and levels of experience and ability;
   b. evaluation of student flight performance;
   c. effective preflight and postflight instruction;
   d. flight instructor responsibilities and certifying procedures;
   e. effective analysis and correction of common student pilot flight errors; and
   f. performance and analysis of standard flight training procedures and maneuvers appropriate to the flight instructor rating sought.

Flight Instruction Records

Each flight instructor shall sign the logbook of each person to whom the instructor has given flight or ground instruction and specify in the logbook the amount of time and date on which the instruction was given. In addition, the instructor shall maintain a record or document containing the following information:

- ☐ The name of each person whose logbook or student pilot certificate has been endorsed for solo flight privileges. The entry must include the type and date of each endorsement.
- ☐ The name of each person for whom the instructor has signed a certification for a written, flight, or practical test, including the kind of test, date of certification, and the results of the test.

All required records must be maintained by the flight instructors for at least three years.

Flight Instructor Limitations

The flight instructor is subject to the following limitations:

1. He may not conduct more than eight hours of flight instruction in any period of 24 consecutive hours.

2. He may not conduct flight instruction in any aircraft that instructor does not hold a Category, Class, and Type Rating.

3. He may not endorse a Student Pilot Certificate for initial solo or solo cross-country flight privileges, unless the instructor has given the student flight instruction and considers the student prepared to conduct the flight safely with the aircraft involved.

4. He may not endorse a student pilot's logbook for solo flight unless he or she has given that student flight instruction and considers the student prepared to conduct the flight safely with the aircraft involved.

5. He may not endorse a student pilot's logbook for solo cross-country flight, unless the instructor has reviewed the student's flight preparation, planning, equipment, and proposed procedures and found them to be adequate for the flight proposed under the existing circumstances.

6. He may not authorize a student pilot to make a solo flight unless the student possess a valid Student Pilot Certificate endorsed for solo in the make and model aircraft to be flown.

7. He may not authorize a student pilot to make a solo cross-country flight unless the student possesses a valid Student Pilot Certificate endorsed for solo cross-country flight in the category of aircraft to be flown.

8. He may not give flight instruction in a multiengine airplane or a helicopter unless the instructor has at least five hours experience as pilot-in-command in the make and model of that airplane or helicopter.

Renewal of Flight Instructor Certificate

A Flight Instructor Certificate may be renewed by the instructor passing the practical test or those portions of the test that the Administrator considers necessary to determine his or her competence as a flight instructor.

The certificate may also be renewed without taking the test if:

- ☐ The instructor's record of instruction shows that the instructor is a competent flight instructor.
- ☐ The instructor has a satisfactory record as a company check pilot, chief flight instructor, or other activity involving the regular evaluation of pilots and passes an oral test that may be required.
- ☐ The instructor has successfully completed, within 90 days before the application for the renewal of his or her certificate, an approved flight instructor refresher course consisting of not less than 24 hours of ground or flight instruction, or both.

Chapter 15

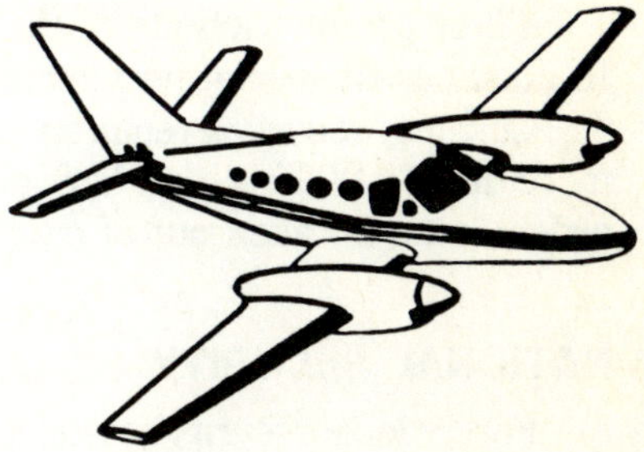

Flying in Foreign Countries

Because of changing political situations, it is always advisable to obtain a thorough briefing on the aviation requirements before flying into or from a foreign country. The rules of flight in most countries are very similar to those observed in the United States, and in most countries, English is the international aviation language.

Most countries require some form of advance notice of arrival. In addition, in most countries there are usage fees for some of the services that U.S. pilots are accustomed to receiving without charge. Pilots should always check a current International Flight Information Manual (IFIM) at the local FAA Flight Service Center before planning a flight into or flying in a foreign country. The manual is designed primarily as a preflight and planning guide for aviators planning flights outside the United States. The IFIM is offered for sale by the Superintendent of Documents, U.S. Government Printing Office, Washington, D.C. 20402. The basic manual is issued annually in April and changes are issued in July, October, and January. (Note: Regional GPO bookstores do not normally have the manual for sale.)

All countries require certain documents to be carried with the aircraft. The standard documents are: certificate of insurance, registration, airworthiness and ownership papers. Proof of U.S. citizenship should be carried at all times when outside the U.S. In those countries that require a visa (a permit to enter and leave a country), the visa may be obtained from that country's embassy or consulate office.

Normally, all aircraft landing in or departing from the U.S. must first land at or finally depart from an international airport. Aircraft registered under the laws of a foreign country not a member of the International Civil Aviation Organization may be navigated in U.S. territory only when authorized by the Department of Transportation.

There are restrictions on the carrying of firearms in and out of the U.S. In most cases, special permits are required.

Currency reporting requirements require a report to the U.S. Customs when more than $5,000 in either U.S. or foreign currency, traveler's checks, money orders, etc., is taken out of or brought into the U.S.

NATIONAL SECURITY

For national security reasons, all aircraft entering or leaving the U.S. must provide identification prior to entry or exit.

An aircraft penetrating a Domestic Air Defense Identification Zone (ADIZ) is required to make position reports. If the pilot is flying in uncontrolled airspace, he is required to report at least 15 minutes before penetration. The following information is required: estimated time, position, and altitude at which the pilot will penetrate. If entering through a Coastal ADIZ, the pilot is also required to report position of the aircraft when it is not less than one hour and not more than two hours average direct cruising distance from the United States.

In most cases, the pilot must have filed a flight plan in order to operate an aircraft in or penetrating a Coastal or Domestic ADIZ. In addition, no person may operate an aircraft in an ADIZ unless the aircraft has a functioning two-way radio.

AUSTRALIA

A passport and visa are required and, for certain areas, yellow fever certificates are required. Private and nonscheduled commercial aircraft overflying or landing for noncommercial purposes need not obtain prior permission.

Australia requires all flights to be able to communicate with and to maintain a listening watch on the appropriate aeronautical station while operating over water in a FIR administered by Australia, whether or not the flight is to be conducted in controlled airspace. Since in some FIRs only SSB (upper sideband) mode is available for communications, alternate arrangements may need to be made. If so, such alternate arrangements must be obtained before departure.

BAHAMAS

Passports and visas are not required for U.S. citizens. Proof of citizenship is required, however. A driver's license is not sufficient identification. Preferred forms of proof include passport (even if expired), birth certificate, U.S. naturalization certificate, or a signed U.S. voter registration card.

Private aircraft overflying or landing for noncommercial purposes need not obtain advance permission. Prior notification, however, is required to the airport of arrival and a flight plan must be on file. Flights conducted between sunset and sunrise must be conducted under IFR rules. No aircraft will be permitted to land or take off at any location in the Bahamas between sunset and sunrise without prior approval for the Director of Civil Aviation.

BARBADOS

Passport and visa are not required for U.S. citizens who have proof of citizenship. Note: Driver's license is not considered as proof. A yellow fever vaccination certificate is required of travellers entering from infected areas.

Private and nonscheduled commercial flights overflying or landing for noncommercial purposes need not obtain prior permission; however, a flight plan must be on file at least 72 hours prior to departure to provide advance notification.

BERMUDA

Passport and visa are not required for U.S. citizens holding proof of citizenship. Note: A driver's license will not suffice as identification. All aircraft must obtain prior permission from the Office of Naval Operations, U.S. Navy, before landing at Bermuda NAS. Since this is the only airport in Bermuda, it serves both military and civil aircraft. There are limited parking facilities in the civil terminal area. Reservations are necessary. Permission to use the parking facilities may be denied if it appears that normal scheduled services cannot be properly accommodated.

In order to avoid congested facilities, the Bermuda Department of Civil Aviation may stipulate specific times for arrival and departure of flights into or out of Bermuda.

Private flights overflying Bermuda do not require prior permission from the Bermuda government.

BRAZIL

Passport and visa are required. A yellow fever vaccination certificate is required for travellers from and to infected areas.

All private and nonscheduled commercial aircraft overflying or landing for noncommercial purposes must give 24 hours prior notice to both the Department of Civil Aviation and to the airport of landing. Prior notifications are valid only after acknowledgement that the notification has been received.

Nonscheduled commercial aircraft landing for commercial purposes must obtain prior permission from the Department of Civil Aviation at least 15 days prior to arrival. Aircraft may remain in Brazil for a maximum of 105 days, but a request for an extension may be made 15 days prior to the expiration of the period.

BRITISH VIRGIN ISLANDS

Passport and visa are not required for U.S. citizens holding proof of citizenship such as birth certificate or signed U.S. voter registration card. Private and nonscheduled commercial aircraft overflying or landing for noncommercial purposes need not obtain prior approval. All nonscheduled commercial aircraft landing for commercial purposes must obtain prior permission from the Director of Civil Aviation. Requests for permission must include all pertinent information concerning the flight.

CANADA

No passport or visa are required. Aliens who are permanent U.S. residents must have their U.S. alien registration card in their possession to return to the U.S. A driver's license is not sufficient identification.

Private aircraft overflying or landing for noncommercial purposes need not obtain prior permission; however, a flight plan must be on file. Non scheduled commercial aircraft landing for commercial purposes must also be licensed or otherwise authorized by the Air Transport Committee of the Canadian Transport Commission, Ottawa, Ontario KIA.

There is a reciprocal agreement for notifying Canadian Customs and Immigration officials via flight plans available for trans-border flights from the U.S. to certain designated Canadian airports. The agreement provides that a pilot, when filing a flight plan for a flight to certain airports, may request that the Customs Service be notified of the expected time of arrival of the aircraft.

Private aircraft are not required to submit a General Declaration with Canadian customs. They are, however, required to make an oral report. In addition, no documents are required for departing Canada.

Some of the Canadian Air Regulations are different from U.S. regulations. Accordingly, a review of their regulations is advised. A tourist who is a holder of a U.S. Pilot Certificate may fly a Canadian registered aircraft after obtaining a Temporary Private Pilot Permit (Tourist) on passing of a written examination on air regulations and air traffic procedures in Canada.

CAYMAN ISLANDS

Passport and visa are not required. Proof of U.S. citizenship is required. Note: A driver's license is not sufficient identification. All private and non-scheduled commercial aircraft overflying or landing for commercial or noncommercial purposes must obtain prior permission from the Director of Civil Aviation. Corporate aircraft are restricted from operating charters on routes used by approved commercial flights.

COSTA RICA

Passport and visa are not required. Tourist cards may be required. Proof of U.S. citizenship is required.

All private and nonscheduled commercial aircraft overflying or landing for noncommercial purposes must provide at least 24 hours advance notification to the Director-General of Civil Aviation. Pilots must have on board the following documents: pilot's license, current medical, aircraft maintenance inspection records, aircraft operations manuals, certificate of airworthiness, and proof of aircraft insurance.

Persons entering on business may be required to present a letter in duplicate stating occupation, purpose of visit, length of stay, and financial responsibility.

CUBA

There is considerable uncertainty in the accuracy and currency of any information on Cuban aviation regulations.

A person may not fly to Cuba from the United States unless the departure is from an international airport of entry, a flight plan has been filed, and a written statement filed within one hour before departure with the office of Immigration and Naturalization Service at the airport of departure. The written statement must contain the following information:

- ☐ All information contained in the flight plan.
- ☐ The name of each occupant of the aircraft.
- ☐ The number of occupants of the aircraft.
- ☐ A description of the cargo, if any.

No person may operate a Cuban-registered aircraft in the United States, except in controlled airspace and in accordance with air traffic clearances or air traffic control instructions that may require use of specific airways or routes and landings at specific airports.

Passport and visa are required. The U.S. Naval Base at Guantanamo Bay is closed to all civil air traffic except for valid emergencies. All emergency landings are thoroughly investigated by U.S. authorities as to their validity and the nature of the business.

DOMINICAN REPUBLIC

Passports are not required. Either a visa or tourist card is required. Note: Proof of U.S. citizenship is required.

Prior permission for private aircraft overflying or landing is not needed, but a flight plan must be on file. All nonscheduled commercial overflying or landing must request prior permission at least 48 hours in advance from the Director General de Aeronautica Civil. Aircraft must have permission to remain in the country more than 30 days. Sale of aviation fuel is limited to 50 percent of the capacity of the aircraft's tanks.

EL SALVADOR

A passport is recommended, but not required. A visa or tourist card is required and both are valid for 90 days. Business travellers must have a letter of recommendation from the firm they represent stating occupation, purpose of visit, length of stay, and financial responsibility.

Prior permission is required for private and nonscheduled commercial flights overflying or landing. Permission may be obtained from the Director General of Civil Aviation, Aeropuerto Internationa de Liopango, San Salvador, El Salvador.

Only those passengers arriving on a nonscheduled flight may depart on the return flight. Landing rights will be denied unless prior permission has been obtained.

JAMAICA

Passport and visa are not required. Proof of U.S. citizenship is required. A driver's license is not sufficient proof.

Prior permission to land or overfly is not needed; however, a flight plan must be on file. Pilots can enter and leave only from an international airport of entry.

MEXICO

A passport is not required for U.S. citizens with proof of citizenship such as a birth certificate, passport, etc. A driver's license is not sufficient as identification. A visa or tourist card is required. Persons entering Mexico on business must have a passport. A visa or tourist card may be obtained from the nearest Mexican Consulate or Mexican Tourism Office. Yellow Fever Vaccination Certificates are required for travellers arriving from or going to an infected area. (Normally this area is considered as south of 22 degrees North Latitude in areas below 1,000 meters elevation. Mexico City is not included.)

Entry Requirements

A flight plan must be on file for all flights in Mexican Territory. Deviations from the flight plan may be punished by fines or confiscation of aircraft. All private aircraft transiting Mexico via coastal cities, both Pacific and Gulf, must give 24 hours advance notice to Mexican authorities.

All private and noncommercial flights into Mexico or overflying must obtain a written permit at least five working days in advance from the Direccion General de Aeronautica Civil, Departmento de Transporte Aerero International, Avendia Universidad y Xola, Mexico City 12, D.F. (Telegraphic address:

Civilair Mexico/telex: 1772526 DGAC ADMIVA MEX) All requests should contain:

- ☐ Name, nationality, address, and business of aircraft operator.
- ☐ Complete route of flight from point of origin to final destination, including airports of landing in Mexico.
- ☐ Purpose of flight.
- ☐ Type, nationality, and registration marks of aircraft and date of aircraft airworthiness certification and certification number.
- ☐ Name, nationalities, and license numbers of crewmembers.
- ☐ Price charged for services in Mexican currency.

In most cases, aircraft rented without pilot will be permitted to enter Mexico provided they are single-engine or twin-engine with a maximum capacity of eight without prior approval noted above, but with approved flight plan.

Mexican regulations require that pilots shall, with suitable advance notice and by means of the most appropriate and expeditious communications system, inform the aviation authorities of their presence at the international airport closest to the point they expect to cross the Mexican border.

On arrival at the airport of entry, pilots shall fill out and sign a form requesting customs and immigration authorization. The form is submitted to the Airport Commandant for approval. The original copy of the form will be returned to the pilot and should be kept aboard the aircraft at all times while in Mexico. The form will be surrendered to officials at the airport of departure.

For a special flight manual on flying in Mexico (Mexico Flight Manual), contact the Texas Aeronautics Commission, P.O. Box 12607, Capitol Station, Austin, TX 78711. In 1986, the cost of the manual was $4.00.

Flying In Mexico

A written flight plan is required for all flights in Mexico. IFR plans are required for all night flights except for the departing flights noted below. Note: Air navigation services in Mexico are not free. For aircraft weighing less than 10,000 kilograms, the charges for these services are included in the price of aviation fuel. Liability insurance is required to protect third parties on the ground. This insurance must be underwritten by a Mexican insurance company.

Departing Mexico

After clearing customs at the airport of departure, no further landings may be made in Mexico. The same crew and passengers that were on board and listed on the entry form must leave when the aircraft departs Mexico unless a change has been approved by the commanding officer of the airfield. It is often difficult to obtain permission for private aircraft to pick up passengers or crewmembers in Mexico who are not listed on the original entry form. In case of a sick or injured person, permission is usually granted to allow him/her to be flown out of Mexico in a private aircraft other than the one in which he/she arrived. Many times, however, only the sick or injured person may fly out. Others may be refused permission to accompany him/her.

Visual night flights are permitted for airplanes leaving the airports of Ciulad Juarez, Matamoros, Nuevo Laredo, Reynosa, Tijuana and Mexicali to fly towards the United States subject to the below conditions.

- ☐ Existing weather conditions shall be visible all along from the departing airport to the destined airport.
- ☐ The flight shall be maintained within the control zone of the leaving airport until the United States border is crossed.
- ☐ The flight shall be concluded with the operational hours of the airport of departure, and radio communications shall be maintained with the air traffic control tower until advised of frequency change.
- ☐ All applicable regulations of international operations are in effect.

UNITED KINGDOM

For landing in the United Kingdom (including Scotland, Wales, Northern Ireland, The Isle of Man and the Channel Islands), a passport is required. No visa is required.

Prior permission is not needed for private and nonscheduled commercial aircraft overflying or landing; a flight plan, however, must be on file. Note: Corporate aircraft must enter as commercial operators. For U.K. customs purposes, company executive or corporate aircraft are not considered as private aircraft.

Chapter 16

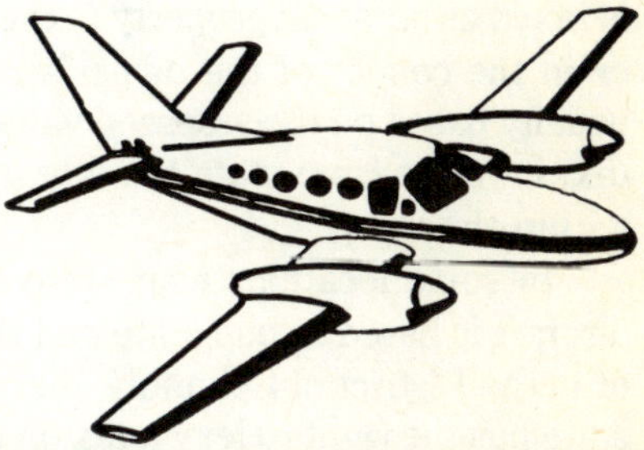

Aviation Taxes

In this chapter, federal and state taxes associated with aviation activities will be discussed.

The Tax Reform Act of 1986 substantially changed the rules regarding the deductibility of aviation-related expenses on federal personal income tax returns. Those changes will also be highlighted in this chapter. Contrary to popular belief, there are still some tax benefits that may be gained if the aviation activities are properly planned.

GASOLINE TAXES

Both states and the federal government tax the sale of gasoline and petroleum products. The amount varies from 6 to 16 cents per gallon. The federal government and most state governments require the aircraft operator to pay these taxes at the time the gas or oil is purchased.

At one time, the aircraft operator could file a form with the federal government for a refund of the gasoline and oil taxes.This was eliminated by a tax change in 1972. If the aircraft is used in business or for business purposes, the gas and oil taxes are most likely deductible. Since they are, however, included in the purchase price of the fuel, normally, the taxes are considered as part of the purchase price of the gas or oil and deducted in that manner. See the discussion later in this chapter on business expenses deductions.

In some states, the gasoline taxes are considered as road and highway taxes. But since airplanes rarely travel on the local roads or highways, the state portion of the taxes may be refundable. Check with your local tax board as to the refundability of these taxes. In those states that refund the taxes, normally they are refundable only to the person who paid the taxes and only upon application with proof of purchase.

PERSONAL PROPERTY TAXES

Since airplanes, like automobiles, are considered as personal property, they may be subject to state or local personal property taxes. Generally, an airplane is taxed as personal property in the county or state where the airplane is based or in the county of the owner's residence. The amounts of these taxes are usually based on the assessed value of the airplane. This being a state or local tax, it varies from state to state (and, in some cases, from county to county within the state).

In some locations near state lines, such as in Washington, D.C., if the aircraft is based in one state and the owner or operator lives in another state or in the District of Columbia, there may be serious questions regarding which state has the right to levy a tax on the aircraft. In these situations, check with a local attorney before paying a personal property tax to either state. If you voluntarily pay the tax to one state and later it is determined that the other state was the proper taxing body, you may be required to pay again. A similar problem may exist when you live in one county and the aircraft is based in another county. The general rule in these cases is that since an aircraft is personal property, it is taxed in the county and state of the owner's residence.

FEDERAL INCOME TAXES

If your aircraft is used mainly for personal flying, then the following expenses may be deducted as personal deduction on your federal income tax return if you itemize, and on some state income tax returns:

1. Any personal property tax paid to a state or local government.
2. Prior to the Tax Reform Act of 1986, any sales tax paid for the purchase of an aircraft or other equipment was deductible as a personal deduction on the federal income tax return. This federal deduction was eliminated effective for tax years beginning after December 31, 1986. A number of states, however, still allow the deduction of sales tax. Check with a local tax person. If the aircraft is used over 50 percent in business, the sales tax may qualify as a business expense. Note below discussion on business expenses.
3. Any portion of the premiums paid on your aviation insurance that is attributed to the cost of medical insurance (hospitalization, etc.) on yourself or members of your family. Note: This deduction was limited by the tax reform act for federal returns by the increased floor (7.5 percent of adjusted gross income) for itemized medical deductions.
4. Any interest paid on loans to finance the purchase of your aircraft or other interest paid. Note: In most cases, this will be classified as nonbusiness

(consumer) interest and therefore subject to limitations as the results of the Tax Reform Act of 1986. The federal income tax deduction for nonbusiness (consumer) interest will be phased out over a five-year period beginning with tax year 1987. In 1987, 65 percent of it will be deductible, 40 percent in 1988, 20 percent in 1989 and 10 percent in 1990. Thereafter, unless there is a modification in the tax law, nonbusiness consumer interest will not be deductible on federal tax returns. In some cases, a home equity loan may be used to finance the aircraft or equipment and that interest may be deductible on your federal return. There are some limitations on this, so check with your tax advisor. As with the deduction on sales tax, if the business purchases the aircraft, the interest deduction is not limited by the nonbusiness consumer interests limitations.

BUSINESS USE OF AIRCRAFT

Where the aircraft is used entirely for business purposes, most of the expenses associated with it are deductible on the federal and state returns. This includes sales tax and interest deductions discussed earlier. The allowable deductions also include a deduction for depreciation. This deduction allows the owner to recapture his investment (recover the cost of the item) in the aircraft or equipment as the items are used.

Investment Credit

The federal investment credit for income tax purposes was cancelled by the Tax Reform Act of 1986. Accordingly, all property placed in service after December 31, 1986, except for the limited cases covered by special transition rules, does not qualify for the credit. Note: Many tax experts predict that this investment tax credit will be reinstated within the next few years.

First Year Expensing

Under the Tax Reform Act, a certain portion of the investment may be recovered by expensing that portion in the first tax year that the equipment or aircraft is placed in service. Expensing is writing off the cost or a portion of it as a current business expense. For tax years 1986 and 1987, a taxpayer may in certain cases expense up to $5,000 of his or her investment. This amount increases for tax years 1988 and 1989 to $7,500 and thereafter to $10,000. For example, if a taxpayer purchases for his business a $50,000 aircraft, he or she may qualify to deduct $10,000 of the purchase price as a current business expense and depreciate the remaining $40,000.

If the aircraft or equipment that has been expensed on a federal income tax return is converted to nonbusiness use within two years of the time the property was placed in service, then a portion of the amount expensed is required to be recaptured as ordinary income. An example of this would be if the taxpayer purchased a used aircraft for his or her business for $20,000 and deducted (expensed) $10,000 on the tax return that year. If less than two years later, that owner converts the aircraft to his or her personal use, the amount expensed ($10,000) would be required to be added to adjusted gross income in the year that the aircraft is converted to personal use. This would only apply if the aircraft is no longer used for business purposes.

Depreciation

If the aircraft or equipment is used over 50 percent of the time in business, it may qualify for a depreciation deduction. If the aircraft or equipment was placed in service (purchased and used) after January 1, 1981, and prior to December 31, 1986, it may be depreciated using the Accelerated Cost Recovery System (ACRS). If the aircraft, etc., was first placed in service after December 31, 1986, it is subject to the modified ACRS.

Under the modified ACRS, the investment may be recovered using the depreciation deduction over a five-year period for light aircraft and similar equipment. The five-year period is, however, subject to be modified by IRS regulations.

Finance Leasing

Prior to the Tax Act of 1986, finance leases were used to finance the purchase of aircraft and equipment. These leases generally provided that the leasee (the person who leases the aircraft) would become the owner of the aircraft at the end of the lease. Under many circumstances, the lessor (person who leased the aircraft) could take advantage of the tax benefits of being the owner of the aircraft during the period of the lease. While these leases still allow a potential owner to purchase an aircraft without a down payment with lease payments less than normal installment payments and are still used to some extent, their popularity has declined significantly with the tax change.

Passive Losses and Lease-Backs

The Tax Reform Act of 1986 placed limits on the deduction of "passive losses" from a federal taxpayer's tax liability. Aircraft lease-backs for the average owner-lessor will be considered as a passive investment for the owner. The 1986 tax change does not allow a taxpayer to deduct losses in excess of his or her income from passive activities. This means that a taxpayer cannot reduce his or her adjusted gross income for federal tax purposes by subtracting these types of losses from earned income.

Passive losses generally are deductible only against income from that or another passive activity. In order not to be considered as a passive activity, the taxpayer must be actively involved in operations on a regular, continuous, and substantial basis. The rule limiting passive losses is phased in over a five-year period beginning with tax year 1987. For tax year 1987, 65 percent of the losses are deductible; for tax year 1988, 40 percent, 20 percent for tax year 1989 and 10 percent in 1990.

Prior to the Tax Reform Act of 1986, the ability to reduce the adjusted gross income of a taxpayer was one of the benefits of aircraft lease-backs. With this loss of tax benefits and the investment tax credit, aircraft lease-backs are not as attractive as in earlier years.

This limitation regarding passive investments do not apply to fixed-based operators or flying schools, since renting aircraft is usually one of their primary activities.

Any passive losses that cannot be deducted in the year in which they occurred may be carried forward to another tax year or deducted in the tax year that the activity is ceased (in case of a lease-back, this would be when the aircraft is sold).

Schedule C

As discussed below, when aviation expenses are deducted as personal deductions, they are subject to the 2 percent adjusted gross income floor and may only be used by taxpayers who itemize. If the taxpayer has a business, then the expenses may be included, if appropriate, on the taxpayer's Schedule C to the federal form 1040. Schedule C is the schedule used for persons involved in a non-corporate form of business. Any aviation expenses that may legally be included on the Schedule C are not subject to the personal deduction limitations noted above.

Company-Owned Aircraft

As noted above, there are definite tax advantages to have the aircraft owned by the company. In addition, if the aircraft is used by non-owner employees and the value of the use is reported as compensation, the company may still deduct the costs involved as business expenses. For example, if a company purchases an aircraft, allows its key employees to use the aircraft, and the use is treated as compensation income to the employees, then the use by the employees will be company business expense and thus 100 percent deductible to the company.

MIXED USE OF AIRCRAFT OR EQUIPMENT

Aviators who use their aircraft for both business and personal use may deduct a percentage of expenses incurred as business expenses if they itemize on their federal tax returns. For example, if you use your aircraft 20 percent of the time for business and 80 percent for personal use, then you may deduct 20 percent as a miscellaneous personal deduction on your federal tax return. Of course, this deduction is available only if you itemize and the total of those deductions is subject to the 2 percent floor of your adjusted gross income.

If your use is mixed, i.e., both business and personal, be sure to include all expenses associated with the aircraft expense including insurance and hangar expense.

When an aircraft owner is required to travel in the course of his or her business, the owner should consider whether it would be possible to fly his or her own aircraft in lieu of commercial aviation. If so, the expenses may be deducted as business expense and the pilot gets the pleasure of flying and the additional aviation experience. In some cases, the non-owner pilot may find it advisable to rent an aircraft for business travel rather than go by commercial carriers. Even an occasional trip to a business convention may be deducted as a business expense, thereby reducing the cost of cross-country training flights.

Appendix I

Regional/Field Offices of the Federal Aviation Administration

Eastern Field Office
New York, New Jersey, Pennsylvania, Delaware, Maryland, West Virginia, Virginia
Federal Building
JFK International Airport
Jamaica, NY 11430

Central
Iowa, Kansas, Missouri, Nebraska
601 E. 12th St.
Kansas City
MO 64106

Great Lakes
Illinois, Indiana, Michigan, Minnesota, North Dakota, Ohio, South Dakota, Wisconsin
2300 E. Devon Ave.
Des Plaines
IL 60018

New England
Maine, Vermont, New Hampshire, Massachusetts, Connecticut, Rhode Island
12 New England Executive Park
Burlington
MA 01803

NorthWest Mountain
Colorado, Idaho, Montana, Oregon, Utah, Washington, Wyoming
17900 Pacific Highway S.
Seattle
WA 98168

Southern
Alabama, Georgia, Florida, Kentucky, Mississippi, North Carolina, Puerto Rico, South Carolina, Tennessee
P.O. Box 20636
Atlanta
GA 30320

SouthWest
Arkansas, Louisiana, New Mexico, Oklahoma, Texas
P.O. Box 1689
Fort Worth
TX 76101

Western-Pacific
Arizona, California, Hawaii, Nevada
P.O. Box 92007
Los Angeles
CA 90009

Alaskan
Alaska
P.O. Box 14
701 C St. Anchorage
AK 99513

Aviation Standards National Field Office
P.O. Box 25082
Oklahoma City
OK 73125

Mike Monroney Aeronautical Center
P.O. Box 25082
Oklahoma City
OK 73125

FAA Technical Center
Atlantic City
NJ 08405

Appendix II

Federal Aviation Regulations, Part 43 Maintenance, Preventive Maintenance, Rebuilding, and Alteration

U.S. Department
of Transportation
Federal Aviation Administration

Federal Aviation Regulations

Part 43
Maintenance, Preventive Maintenance, Rebuilding, and Alteration

Published
January 1974

Consolidated Reprint
This consolidated reprint incorporates:
Changes 1 through 7
as of 10/1/86

Part 43—Maintenance, Preventive Maintenance, Rebuilding, and Alteration

Contents

Appendixes

Part 43—Maintenance, Preventive Maintenance, Rebuilding, and Alteration

§ 43.1 Applicability.

(a) Except as provided in paragraph (b), this Part prescribes rules governing the maintenance, preventive maintenance, rebuilding, and alteration of any—

[(1) Aircraft having a U.S. airworthiness certificate;

[(2) Foreign-registered civil aircraft used in common carriage or carriage of mail under the provisions of Part 121, 127, or 135 of this chapter; and

[(3) Airframe, aircraft engines, propellers, appliances, and component parts of such aircraft.]

(b) This Part does not apply to any aircraft for which an experimental airworthiness certificate has been issued, unless a different kind of airworthiness certificate had previously been issued for that aircraft.

[§ 43.2 Records of overhaul and rebuilding.

[(a) No person may describe in any required maintenance entry or form an aircraft, airframe, aircraft engine, propeller, appliance, or component part as being overhauled unless—

[(1) Using methods, techniques, and practices acceptable to the Administrator, it has been disassembled, cleaned, inspected, repaired as necessary, and reassembled; and

[(2) It has been tested in accordance with approved standards and technical data, or in accordance with current standards and technical data acceptable to the Administrator, which have been developed and documented by the holder of the type certificate, supplemental type certificate, or a material, part, process, or appliance approval under § 21.305 of this chapter.

[(b) No person may describe in any required maintenance entry or form an aircraft, airframe, aircraft engine, propeller, appliance, or component part as being rebuilt unless it has been disassembled, cleaned, inspected, repaired as necessary, reassembled, and tested to the same tolerances and limits as a new item, using either new parts or used parts that either conform to new part tolerances and limits or to approved oversized or undersized dimensions.]

§ 43.3 Persons authorized to perform maintenance, preventive maintenance, rebuilding, and alterations.

[(a) Except as provided in this section and § 43.17, no person may maintain, rebuild, alter, or perform preventive maintenance on an aircraft, airframe, aircraft engine, propeller, appliance, or component part to which this Part applies.] Those items, the performance of which is a major alteration, a major repair, or preventive maintenance, are listed in Appendix A.

(b) The holder of a mechanic certificate may perform maintenance, preventive maintenance, and alterations as provided in Part 65.

(c) The holder of a repairman certificate may perform maintenance and preventive maintenance as provided in Part 65.

(d) A person working under the supervision of a holder of a mechanic or repairman certificate may perform the maintenance, preventive maintenance, and alterations that his supervisor is authorized to perform, if the supervisor personally observes the work being done to the extent necessary to ensure that it is being done properly and if the supervisor is readily available, in person, for consultation. [However, this paragraph does not authorize the performance of any inspection required by Part 91 or Part 125 of this chapter or any inspection performed after a major repair or alteration.]

(e) The holder of a repair station certificate may perform maintenance, preventive maintenance, and alterations as provided in Part 145.

(f) The holder of an air carrier operating certificate or an operating certificate issued under Part 121, 127, or 135, may perform maintenance, preventive maintenance, and alterations as provided in Part 121, 127, or 135.

(g) The holder of a pilot certificate issued under Part 61 may perform preventive maintenance on any aircraft owned or operated by that pilot which is not used under Part 121, 127, 129, or 135.

[(h) Notwithstanding the provisions of paragraph (g) of this section, the Administrator may approve a certificate holder under Part 135 of this chapter, operating rotorcraft in a remote area, to allow a pilot to perform specific preventive maintenance items provided—

[(1) The items of preventive maintenance are a result of a known or suspected mechanical difficulty or malfunction that occurred en route to or in a remote area;

[(2) The pilot has satisfactorily completed an approved training program and is authorized in writing by the certificate holder for each item of preventive maintenance that the pilot is authorized to perform;

[(3) There is no certificated mechanic available to perform preventive maintenance;

[(4) The certificate holder has procedures to evaluate the accomplishment of a preventive maintenance item that requires a decision concerning the airworthiness of the rotorcraft; and

[(5) The items of preventive maintenance authorized by this section are those listed in paragraph (c) of Appendix A of this Part.]

[(i)] A manufacturer may—

(1) Rebuild or alter any aircraft, aircraft engine, propeller, or appliance manufactured by him under a type or production certificate;

(2) Rebuild or alter any appliance or part of aircraft, aircraft engines, propellers, or appliances manufactured by him under a Technical Standard Order Authorization, an FAA-Parts Manufacturer Approval, or Product and Process Specification issued by the Administrator; and

(3) Perform any inspection required by Part 91 or Part 125 of this chapter on aircraft it manufactures, while currently operating under a production certificate or under a currently approved production inspection system for such aircraft.

§ 43.5 Approval for return to service after maintenance, preventive maintenance, rebuilding, or alteration.

No person may approve for return to service any aircraft, airframe, aircraft engine, propeller, or appliance, that has undergone maintenance, preventive maintenance, rebuilding, or alteration unless—

(a) The maintenance record entry required by § 43.9 or § 43.11, as appropriate, has been made;

(b) The repair or alteration form authorized by or furnished by the Administrator has been executed in a manner prescribed by the Administrator; and

(c) If a repair or an alteration results in any change in the aircraft operating limitations or flight data contained in the approved aircraft flight manual, those operating limitations or flight data are appropriately revised and set forth as prescribed in § 91.31.

§ 43.7 Persons authorized to approve aircraft, airframes, aircraft engines, propellers, appliances, or component parts for return to service after maintenance, preventive maintenance, rebuilding, or alteration.

(a) Except as provided in this section and § 43.17, no person, other than the Administrator, may approve an aircraft, airframe, aircraft engine, propeller, appliance, or component part for return to service after it has undergone maintenance, preventive maintenance, rebuilding, or alteration.

(b) The holder of a mechanic certificate or an inspection authorization may approve an aircraft, airframe, aircraft engine, propeller, appliance, or component part for return to service as provided in Part 65 of this chapter.

(c) The holder of a repair station certificate may approve an aircraft, airframe, aircraft engine, propeller, appliance, or component part for return to service as provided in Part 145 of this chapter.

(d) A manufacturer may approve for return to service any aircraft, airframe, aircraft engine, propeller, appliance, or component part which that manufacturer has worked on under § 43.3(h). However, except for minor alterations, the work must have been done in accordance with technical data approved by the Administrator.

(e) The holder of an air carrier operating certificate or an operating certificate issued under Part 121, 127, or 135, may approve an aircraft, airframe, aircraft engine, propeller, appliance, or component part for return to service as provided in Part 121, 127, or 135 of this chapter, as applicable.

(f) A person holding at least a private pilot certificate may approve an aircraft for return to service after performing preventive maintenance under the provisions of § 43.3(g).

§ 43.9 Content, form, and disposition of maintenance, preventive maintenance, rebuilding, and alteration records (except inspections performed in accordance with Part 91, Part 123, Part 125, § 135.411(a) (1), and § 135.419 of this chapter).

(a) *Maintenance record entries.* Except as provided in paragraphs (b) and (c) of this section, each person who maintains, performs preventive maintenance, rebuilds, or alters an aircraft, airframe, aircraft engine, propeller, appliance, or component part shall make an entry in the maintenance record of that equipment containing the following information:

(1) A description (or reference to data acceptable to the Administrator) of work performed.

(2) The date of completion of the work performed.

(3) The name of the person performing the work if other than the person specified in paragraph (a) (4) of this section.

(4) If the work performed on the aircraft, airframe, aircraft engine, propeller, appliance, or component part has been performed satisfactorily, the signature, certificate number, and kind of certificate held by the person approving the work. The signature constitutes the approval for return to service only for the work performed.

In addition to the entry required by this paragraph, major repairs and major alterations shall be entered on a form, and the form disposed of, in the manner prescribed in Appendix B, by the person performing the work.

(b) Each holder of an air carrier operating certificate or an operating certificate issued under Part 121, 127, or 135, that is required by its approved operations specifications to provide for a continuous airworthiness maintenance program, shall make a record of the maintenance, preventive maintenance, rebuilding, and alteration, on aircraft, airframes, aircraft engines, propellers, appliances, or component parts which it operates in accordance with the applicable provisions of Part 121, 127, or 135 of this chapter, as appropriate.

(c) This section does not apply to persons performing inspections in accordance with Part 91, 123, 125, § 135.411(a) (1), or § 135.419 of this chapter.

(Approved by the Office of Management and Budget under OMB control number 2120–0020)

§ 43.11 Content, form, and disposition of the records for inspections conducted under Parts 91, 123, 125, § 135.411(a) (1), and § 135.419 of this chapter.

(a) *Maintenance record entries.* The person approving or disapproving for return to service an aircraft, airframe, aircraft engine, propeller, appliance, or component part after any inspection performed in accordance with Part 91, 123, 125, § 135.411(a) (1), or § 135.419 shall make an entry in the maintenance record of that equipment containing the following information:

(1) The type of inspection and a brief description of the extent of the inspection.

(2) The date of the inspection and aircraft total time in service.

(3) The signature, the certificate number, and kind of certificate held by the person approving or disapproving for return to service

the aircraft, airframe, aircraft engine, propeller, appliance, component part, or portions thereof.

(4) Except for progressive inspections, if the aircraft is found to be airworthy and approved for return to service, the following or a similarly worded statement—"I certify that this aircraft has been inspected in accordance with (insert type) inspection and was determined to be in airworthy condition."

(5) Except for progressive inspections, if the aircraft is not approved for return to service because of needed maintenance, noncompliance with applicable specifications, airworthiness directives, or other approved data, the following or a similarly worded statement—"I certify that this aircraft has been inspected in accordance with (insert type) inspection and a list of discrepancies and unairworthy items dated (date) has been provided for the aircraft owner or operator."

(6) For progressive inspections, the following or a similarly worded statement—"I certify that in accordance with a progressive inspection program, a routine inspection of (identify whether aircraft or components) and a detailed inspection of (identify components) were performed and the (aircraft or components) are (approved or disapproved) for return to service." If disapproved, the entry will further state "and a list of discrepancies and unairworthy items dated (date) has been provided to the aircraft owner or operator."

(7) If an inspection is conducted under an inspection program provided for in Part 91, 123, 125, or § 135.411(a) (1), the entry must identify the inspection program, that part of the inspection program accomplished, and contain a statement that the inspection was performed in accordance with the inspections and procedures for that particular program.

(b) *Listing of discrepancies.* If the person performing any inspection required by Part 91, 123, 125, or § 135.411(a) (1) of this chapter finds that the aircraft is unairworthy or does not meet the applicable type certificate data, airworthiness directives, or other approved data upon which its airworthiness depends, that person must give the owner or lessee a signed and dated list of those discrepancies.

(Approved by the Office of Management and Budget under OMB control number 2120-0020)

§ 43.12 Maintenance records: falsification, reproduction, or alteration.

(a) No person may make or cause to be made:

(1) Any fraudulent or intentionally false entry in any record or report that is required to be made, kept, or used to show compliance with any requirement under this Part;

(2) Any reproduction, for fraudulent purpose, of any record or report under this Part; or

(3) Any alteration, for fraudulent purpose, of any record or report under this Part.

(b) The commission by any person of an act prohibited under paragraph (a) of this section is a basis for suspending or revoking the applicable airman, operator, or production certificate, Technical Standard Order Authorization, FAA-Parts Manufacturer Approval, or Product and Process Specification issued by the Administrator and held by that person.

§ 43.13 Performance rules (general).

(a) Each person performing maintenance, alteration, or preventive maintenance on an aircraft, engine, propeller, or appliance shall use the methods, techniques, and practices prescribed in the current manufacturer's maintenance manual or Instructions for Continued Airworthiness prepared by its manufacturer, or other methods, techniques, and practices acceptable to the Administrator, except as noted in § 43.16. He shall use the tools, equipment, and test apparatus necessary to assure completion of the work in accordance with accepted industry practices. If special equipment or test apparatus is recommended by the manufacturer involved, he must use that equipment or apparatus or its equivalent acceptable to the Administrator.

(b) Each person maintaining or altering, or performing preventive maintenance, shall do that work in such a manner and use materials of such a quality, that the condition of the aircraft, airframe, aircraft engine, propeller, or appliance worked on will be at least equal to its original or properly altered condition (with regard to aerodynamic function, structural strength, resistance to vibration and deterioration, and other qualities affecting airworthiness).

(c) *Special provisions for holders of air carrier operating certificates and operating certificates issued under the provisions of Part 121, 127, or 135.* Unless otherwise notified by the Administrator, the methods, techniques, and practices contained in the maintenance manual or the maintenance part of the manual of the holder of an air carrier operating certificate or an operating certificate under Part 121, 127, or 135 (that is required by its operating specifications to provide a continuous airworthiness maintenance and inspection program) constitute acceptable means of compliance with this section.

(d) [Deleted.

§ 43.15 Additional performance rules for inspections.

(a) *General.* Each person performing an inspection required by Part 91, 123, 125, or 135 of this chapter, shall—

(1) Perform the inspection so as to determine whether the aircraft, or portion(s) thereof under inspection, meets all applicable airworthiness requirements; and

(2) If the inspection is one provided for in Part 123, 125, 135, or § 91.169(e) of this chapter, perform the inspection in accordance with the instructions and procedures set forth in the inspection program for the aircraft being inspected.

(b) *Rotorcraft.* Each person performing an inspection required by Part 91 on a rotorcraft shall inspect the following systems in accordance with the maintenance manual or Instructions for Continued Airworthiness of the manufacturer concerned:

(1) The drive shafts or similar systems.

(2) The main rotor transmission gear box for obvious defects.

(3) The main rotor and center section (or the equivalent area).

(4) The auxiliary rotor on helicopters.

(c) *Annual and 100-hour inspections.*

(1) Each person performing an annual or 100-hour inspection shall use a checklist while performing the inspection. The checklist may be of the person's own design, one provided by the manufacturer of the equipment being inspected, or one obtained from another source. This checklist must include the scope and detail of the items contained in Appendix D to this Part and paragraph (b) of this section.

[(2) Each person approving a reciprocating-engine-powered aircraft for return to service after an annual or 100-hour inspection shall, before that approval, run the aircraft engine or engines to determine satisfactory performance, in accordance with the manufacturer's recommendations, of—]

(i) Power output (static and idle r.p.m.);

(ii) Magnetos;

(iii) Fuel and oil pressure; and

(iv) Cylinder and oil temperature.

[(3) Each person approving a turbine-engine-powered aircraft for return to service after an annual, 100-hour, progressive inspection shall, before that approval, run the aircraft engine or engines to determine satisfactory performance in accordance with the manufacturer's recommendations.]

(d) *Progressive inspection.*

(1) Each person performing a progressive inspection shall, at the start of a progressive inspection system, inspect the aircraft completely. After this initial inspection, routine and detailed inspections must be conducted as prescribed in the progressive inspection schedule. Routine inspections consist of visual examination or check of the appliances, the aircraft, and its components and systems, insofar as practicable without disassembly. Detailed inspections consist of a thorough examination of the appliances, the aircraft, and its components and systems, with such disassembly as is necessary. For the purposes of

this subparagraph, the overhaul of a component or system is considered to be a detailed inspection.

(2) If the aircraft is away from the station where inspections are normally conducted, an appropriately rated mechanic, a certificated repair station, or the manufacturer of the aircraft may perform inspections in accordance with the procedures and using the forms of the person who would otherwise perform the inspection.

§ 43.16 Airworthiness Limitations.

Each person performing an inspection or other maintenance specified in an Airworthiness Limitations section of a manufacturer's maintenance manual or Instructions for Continued Airworthiness shall perform the inspection or other maintenance in accordance with that section, or in accordance with operations specifications approved by the Administrator under Parts 121, 123, 127, or 135, or an inspection program approved under § 91.169(e).

§ 43.17 Mechanical work performed on U.S. registered aircraft by certain Canadian persons.

(a) A person holding a valid mechanic certificate of competence (Aircraft Maintenance Engineer license) and appropriate ratings issued by the Canadian Government, or a person who is an authorized employee (Approved Inspector) performing work for a company whose system of quality control for the inspection and maintenance of aircraft has been approved by the Canadian Department of Transport may, in connection with aircraft of U.S. registry in Canada:

(1) Perform maintenance, preventive maintenance and alterations if those operations are done in accordance with § 43.13 and the maintenance record entries are made in accordance with § 43.9.

(2) Except for an annual inspection, perform any inspection required by § 91.169 of this chapter, if the inspection is done in accordance with § 43.15 and the maintenance record entries are made in accordance with § 43.11.

(3) Approve (certify) maintenance, preventive maintenance, and alterations performed under this section except that a Canadian Aircraft Maintenance Engineer may not approve a major repair or major alteration.

(b) A Canadian Department of Transport Airworthiness Inspector, or an authorized employee (Approved Inspector) performing work for a company approved by the Canadian Department of Transport, may approve (certify) a major repair or major alteration performed under this section if the work was done in accordance with technical data approved by the Administrator.

(c) No person may operate in air commerce an aircraft, airframe, aircraft engine, propeller, or appliance on which maintenance, preventive maintenance, or alteration has been performed under this section unless it has been approved by a person authorized in this section.

NOTE.—The recordkeeping and reporting requirements contained herein have been approved by the Bureau of the Budget in accordance with the Federal Reports Act of 1942.

Appendix A

Major Alterations, Major Repairs, and Preventive Maintenance

(a) *Major alterations.*

(1) *Airframe major alterations.* Alterations of the following parts and alterations of the following types, when not listed in the aircraft specifications issued by the FAA, are airframe major alterations:

(i) Wings.

(ii) Tail surfaces.

(iii) Fuselage.

(iv) Engine mounts.

(v) Control system.

(vi) Landing gear.

(vii) Hull or floats.

(viii) Elements of an airframe including spars, ribs, fittings, shock absorbers, bracing, cowlings, fairings, and balance weights.

(ix) Hydraulic and electrical actuating system of components.

(x) Rotor blades.

(xi) Changes to the empty weight or empty balance which result in an increase in the maximum certificated weight or center of gravity limits of the aircraft.

(xii) Changes to the basic design of the fuel, oil, cooling, heating, cabin presssurization, electrical, hydraulic, de-icing, or exhaust systems.

(xiii) Changes to the wing or to fixed or movable control surfaces which affect flutter and vibration characteristics.

(2) *Powerplant major alterations.* The following alterations of a powerplant when not listed in the engine specifications issued by the FAA, are powerplant major alterations:

(i) Conversion of an aircraft engine from one approved model to another, involving any changes in compression ratio, propeller reduction gear, impeller gear ratios or the substitution of major engine parts which requires extensive rework and testing of the engine.

(ii) Changes to the engine by replacing aircraft engine structural parts with parts not supplied by the original manufacturer or parts not specifically approved by the Administrator.

(iii) Installation of an accessory which is not approved for the engine.

(iv) Removal of accessories that are listed as required equipment on the aircraft or engine specification.

(v) Installation of structural parts other than the type of parts approved for the installation.

(vi) Conversions of any sort for the purpose of using fuel of a rating or grade other than that listed in the engine specifications.

(3) *Propeller major alterations.* The following alterations of a propeller when not authorized in the propeller specifications issued by the FAA are propeller major alterations:

(i) Changes in blade design.

(ii) Changes in hub design.

(iii) Changes in the governor or control design.

(iv) Installation of a propeller governor or feathering system.

(v) Installation of propeller de-icing system.

(vi) Installation of parts not approved for the propeller.

(4) *Appliance major alterations.* Alterations of the basic design not made in accordance with recommendations of the appliance manufacturer or in accordance with an FAA Airworthiness Directive are appliance major alterations. In addition, changes in the basic design of radio communication and

navigation equipment approved under type certification or a Technical Standard Order that have an effect on frequency stability, noise level, sensitivity, selectivity, distortion, spurious radiation, AVC characteristics, or ability to meet environmental test conditions and other changes that have an effect on the performance of the equipment are also major alterations.

(b) *Major repairs.*

(1) *Airframe major repairs.* Repairs to the following parts of an airframe and repairs of the following types, involving the strengthening, reinforcing, splicing, and manufacturing of primary structural members or their replacement, when replacement is by fabrication such as riveting or welding, are airframe major repairs:

(i) Box beams.

(ii) Monocoque or semimonocoque wings or control surfaces.

(iii) Wing stringers or chord members.

(iv) Spars.

(v) Spar flanges.

(vi) Members of truss-type beams.

(vii) Thin sheet webs of beams.

(viii) Keel and chine members of boat hulls or floats.

(ix) Corrugated sheet compression members which act as flange material of wings or tail surfaces.

(x) Wing main ribs and compression members.

(xi) Wing or tail surface brace struts.

(xii) Engine mounts.

(xiii) Fuselage longerons.

(xiv) Members of the side truss, horizontal truss, or bulkheads.

(xv) Main seat support braces and brackets.

(xvi) Landing gear brace struts.

(xvii) Axles.

(xviii) Wheels.

(xix) Skis, and ski pedestals.

(xx) Parts of the control system such as control columns, pedals, shafts, brackets, or horns.

(xxi) Repairs involving the substitution of material.

(xxii) The repair of damaged areas in metal or plywood stressed covering exceeding six inches in any direction.

(xxiii) The repair of portions of skin sheets by making additional seams.

(xxiv) The splicing of skin sheets.

(xxv) The repair of three or more adjacent wing or control surface ribs or the leading edge of wings and control surfaces, between such adjacent ribs.

(xxvi) Repair of fabric covering involving an area greater than that required to repair two adjacent ribs.

(xxvii) Replacement of fabric on fabric covered parts such as wings, fuselages, stabilizers, and control surfaces.

(xxviii) Repairing, including rebottoming, of removable or integral fuel tanks and oil tanks.

(2) *Powerplant major repairs.* Repairs of the following parts of an engine and repairs of the following types, are powerplant major repairs:

(i) Separation or disassembly of a crankcase or crankshaft of a reciprocating engine equipped with an integral supercharger.

(ii) Separation or disassembly of a crankcase or crankshaft of a reciprocating engine equipped with other than spurtype propeller reduction gearing.

(iii) Special repairs to structural engine parts by welding, plating, metalizing, or other methods.

(3) *Propeller major repairs.* Repairs of the following types to a propeller are propeller major repairs:

(i) Any repairs to, or straightening of steel blades.

(ii) Repairing or machining of steel hubs.

(iii) Shortening of blades.

(iv) Retipping of wood propellers.

(v) Replacement of outer laminations on fixed-pitch wood propellers.

(vi) Repairing elongated bolt holes in the hub of fixed-pitch wood propellers.

(vii) Inlay work on wood blades.

(viii) Repairs to composition blades.

(ix) Replacement of tip fabric.

(x) Replacement of plastic covering.

(xi) Repair of propeller governors.

(xii) Overhaul of controllable pitch propellers.

(xiii) Repairs to deep dents, cuts, scars, nicks, etc., and straightening of aluminum blades.

(xiv) The repair or replacement of internal elements of blades.

(4) *Appliance major repairs.* Repairs of the following types to appliances are appliance major repairs:

(i) Calibration and repair of instruments.

(ii) Calibration of radio equipment.

(iii) Rewinding the field coil of an electrical accessory.

(iv) Complete disassembly of complex hydraulic power valves.

(v) Overhaul of pressure type carburetors, and pressure type fuel, oil, and hydraulic pumps.

(c) *Preventive maintenance.* Preventive maintenance is limited to the following work, provided it does not involve complex assembly operations:

(1) Removal, installation, and repair of landing gear tires.

(2) Replacing elastic shock absorber cords on landing gear.

(3) Servicing landing gear shock struts by adding oil, air, or both.

(4) Servicing landing gear wheel bearings, such as cleaning and greasing.

(5) Replacing defective safety wiring or cotter keys.

(6) Lubrication not requiring disassembly other than removal of nonstructural items such as cover plates, cowlings, and fairings.

(7) Making simple fabric patches not requiring rib stitching or the removal of structural parts or control surfaces. In the case of balloons, the making of small fabric repairs to envelopes (as defined in, and in accordance with, the balloon manufacturers' instructions) not requiring load tape repair or replacement.

(8) Replenishing hydraulic fluid in the hydraulic reservoir.

(9) Refinishing decorative coating of fuselage, balloon baskets, wings, tail group surfaces (excluding balanced control surfaces), fairings, cowlings, landing gear, cabin, or cockpit interior when removal or disassembly of any primary structure or operating system is not required.

(10) Applying preservative or protective material to components where no disassembly of any primary structure or operating system is involved and where such coating is not prohibited or is not contrary to good practices.

(11) Repairing upholstery and decorative furnishings of the cabin, cockpit, or balloon interior when the repairing does not require disassembly of any primary structure or operating system or interfere with an operating system or affect primary structure of the aircraft.

(12) Making small simple repairs to fairings, nonstructural cover plates, cowlings, and small patches and reinforcements not changing the contour so as to interfere with proper airflow.

(13) Replacing side windows where that work does not interfere with the structure or any operating system such as controls, electrical equipment, etc.

(14) Replacing safety belts.

(15) Replacing seats or seat parts with replacement parts approved for the aircraft, not involving disassembly of any primary structure or operating system.

(16) Trouble shooting and repairing broken circuits in landing light wiring circuits.

(17) Replacing bulbs, reflectors, and lenses of position and landing lights.

(18) Replacing wheels and skis where no weight and balance computation is involved.

(19) Replacing any cowling not requiring removal of the propeller or disconnection of flight controls.

(20) Replacing or cleaning spark plugs and setting of spark plug gap clearance.

(21) Replacing any hose connection except hydraulic connections.

(22) Replacing prefabricated fuel lines.

【(23) Cleaning or replacing fuel and oil strainers or filter elements.】

(24) Replacing and servicing batteries.

(25) Removing and installing glider wings and tail surfaces that are specifically designed

for quick removal and installation and when such removal and installation can be accomplished by the pilot.

(26) Cleaning of balloon burner pilot and main nozzles in accordance with the balloon manufacturer's instructions.

(27) Replacement or adjustment of nonstructural standard fasteners incidental to operations.

(28) Removing and installing balloon baskets and burners that are specifically designed for quick removal and installations and when such removal and installation can be accomplished by the pilot, provided that baskets are not interchanged except as provided in the type certificate data sheet for that balloon.

(29) The installation of anti-misfueling devices to reduce the diameter of fuel tank filler openings provided the specific device has been made a part of the aircraft type certificate data by the aircraft manufacturer, the aircraft manufacturer has provided FAA-approved instructions for installation of the specific device, and installation does not involve the disassembly of the existing tank filler opening.

[(30) Removing, checking, and replacing magnetic chip detectors.]

Appendix B

Recording of Major Repairs and Major Alterations

(a) Except as provided in paragraphs (b) and (c), each person performing a major repair or major alteration shall—

(1) Execute FAA Form 337 at least in duplicate;

(2) Give a signed copy of that form to the aircraft owner; and

(3) Forward a copy of that form to the local FAA District Office within 48 hours after the aircraft, airframe, aircraft engine, propeller, or appliance is approved for return to service.

(b) For major repairs made in accordance with a manual or specification acceptable to the Administrator, a certificated repair station may, in place of the requirements of paragraph (a)—

(1) Use the customer's work order upon which the repair is recorded;

(2) Give the aircraft owner a signed copy of the work order and retain a duplicate copy for a least 2 years from the date of approval for return to service of the aircraft, airframe, aircraft engine, propeller, or appliance;

(3) Give the aircraft owner a maintenance release signed by an authorized representative of the repair station and incorporating the following information:

(i) Identity of the aircraft, airframe, aircraft engine, propeller, or appliance.

(ii) If an aircraft, the make, model, serial number, nationality and registration marks, and location of the repaired area.

(iii) If an airframe, aircraft engine, propeller, or appliance, give the manufacturer's name, name of the part, model, and serial numbers (if any); and

(4) Include the following or a similarly worded statement—

"The aircraft, airframe, aircraft engine, propeller, or appliance identified above was repaired and inspected in accordance with current Regulations of the Federal Aviation Administration and is approved for return to service.

"Pertinent details of the repair are on file at this repair station under Order No. ______. Date ______

Signed ______________________ for
(signature of authorized representative)

______________________ ______________
(repair station name) (certificate no.)

______________________."
(address)

(c) For a major repair or major alteration made by a person authorized in § 43.17, the person who performs the major repair or major alteration and the person authorized by § 43.17 to approve that work shall execute a FAA Form 337 at least in duplicate. A completed copy of that form shall be—

(1) Given to the aircraft owner; and

(2) Forwarded to the Federal Aviation Administration, Aircraft Registration Branch, P.O. Box 25082, Oklahoma City, Oklahoma 73125, within 48 hours after the work is inspected.

Appendix C
[Revoked]

Appendix D

Scope and Detail of Items (as Applicable to the Particular Aircraft) to be Included in Annual and 100-Hour Inspections

(a) Each person performing an annual or 100-hour inspection shall, before that inspection, remove or open all necessary inspection plates, access doors, fairing, and cowling. He shall thoroughly clean the aircraft and aircraft engine.

(b) Each person performing an annual or 100-hour inspection shall inspect (where applicable) the following components of the fuselage and hull group:

(1) Fabric and skin—for deterioration, distortion, other evidence of failure, and defective or insecure attachment of fittings.

(2) Systems and components—for improper installation, apparent defects, and unsatisfactory operation.

(3) Envelope, gas bags, ballast tanks, and related parts—for poor condition.

(c) Each person performing an annual or 100-hour inspection shall inspect (where applicable) the following components of the cabin and cockpit group:

(1) Generally—for uncleanliness and loose equipment that might foul the controls.

(2) Seats and safety belts—for poor condition and apparent defects.

(3)' Windows and windshields—for deterioration and breakage.

(4) Instruments—for poor condition, mounting, marking, and (where practicable) for improper operation.

(5) Flight and engine controls—for improper installation and improper operation.

(6) Batteries—for improper installation and improper charge.

(7) All systems—for improper installation, poor general condition, apparent and obvious defects, and insecurity of attachment.

(d) Each person performing an annual or 100-hour inspection shall inspect (where applicable) components of the engine and nacelle group as follows:

(1) Engine section—for visual evidence of excessive oil, fuel, or hydraulic leaks, and sources of such leaks.

(2) Studs and nuts—for improper torquing and obvious defects.

(3) Internal engine—for cylinder compression and for metal particles or foreign matter on screens and sump drain plugs. If there is weak cylinder compression, for improper internal condition and improper internal tolerances.

(4) Engine mount—for cracks, looseness of mounting, and looseness of engine to mount.

(5) Flexible vibration dampeners—for poor condition and deterioration.

(6) Engine controls—for defects, improper travel, and improper safetying.

(7) Lines, hoses, and clamps—for leaks, improper condition, and looseness.

(8) Exhaust stacks—for cracks, defects, and improper attachment.

(9) Accessories—for apparent defects in security of mounting.

(10) All systems—for improper installation, poor general condition, defects, and insecure attachment.

(11) Cowling—for cracks, and defects.

(e) Each person performing an annual or 100-hour inspection shall inspect (where applicable) the following components of the landing gear group:

(1) All units—for poor condition and insecurity of attachment.

(2) Shock absorbing devices—for improper oleo fluid level.

(3) Linkage, trusses, and members—for undue or excessive wear, fatigue, and distortion.

(4) Retracting and locking mechanism—for improper operation.

(5) Hydraulic lines—for leakage.

(6) Electrical system—for chafing and improper operation of switches.

(7) Wheels—for cracks, defects, and condition of bearings.

(8) Tires—for wear and cuts.

(9) Brakes—for improper adjustment.

(10) Floats and skis—for insecure attachment and obvious or apparent defects.

(f) Each person performing an annual or 100-hour inspection shall inspect (where applicable) all components of the wing and center section assembly for poor general condition, fabric or skin deterioration, distortion, evidence of failure, and insecurity of attachment.

(g) Each person performing an annual or 100-hour inspection shall inspect (where applicable) all components and systems that make up the complete empennage assembly for poor general condition, fabric or skin deterioration, distortion, evidence of failure, insecure attachment, improper component installation, and improper component operation.

(h) Each person performing an annual or 100-hour inspection shall inspect (where applicable) the following components of the propeller group:

(1) Propeller assembly—for cracks, nicks, binds, and oil leakage.

(2) Bolts—for improper torquing and lack of safetying.

(3) Anti-icing devices—for improper operations and obvious defects.

(4) Control mechanisms—for improper operation, insecure mounting, and restricted travel.

(i) Each person performing an annual or 100-hour inspection shall inspect (where applicable) the following components of the radio group:

(1) Radio and electronic equipment—for improper installation and insecure mounting.

(2) Wiring and conduits—for improper routing, insecure mounting, and obvious defects.

(3) Bonding and shielding—for improper installation and poor condition.

(4) Antenna including trailing antenna—for poor condition, insecure mounting, and improper operation.

(j) Each person performing an annual or 100-hour inspection shall inspect (where applicable) each installed miscellaneous item that is not otherwise covered by this listing for improper installation and improper operation.

Appendix E

Altimeter System Test and Inspection

Each person performing the altimeter system tests and inspections required by § 91.171 shall comply with the following:

(a) Static pressure system:

(1) Ensure freedom from entrapped moisture and restrictions.

(2) Determine that leakage is within the tolerances established in § 23.1325 or § 25.1325, whichever is applicable.

(3) Determine that the static port heater, if installed, is operative.

(4) Ensure that no alterations or deformation of the airframe surface have been made that would affect the relationship between air pressure in the static pressure system and true ambient static air pressure for any flight condition.

(b) Altimeter:

(1) Test by an appropriately rated repair facility in accordance with the following subparagraphs. Unless otherwise specified, each test for performance may be conducted with the instrument subjected to vibration. When tests are conducted with the temperature substantially different from ambient temperature of approximately 25 degrees C., allowance shall be made for the variation from the specified condition.

(i) *Scale error*—With the barometric pressure scale at 29.92 inches of mercury, the altimeter shall be subjected successively to pressures corresponding to the altitude specified in Table I up to the maximum normally expected operating altitude of the airplane in which the altimeter is to be installed. The reduction in pressure shall be made at a rate not in excess of 20,000 feet per minute to within approximately 2,000 feet of the test point. The test point shall be approached at a rate compatible with the test equipment. The altimeter shall be kept at the pressure corresponding to each test point for at least one minute, but not more than ten minutes, before a reading is taken. The error at all test points must not exceed the tolerances specified in Table I.

(ii) *Hysteresis*—The hysteresis test shall begin not more than 15 minutes after the altimeter's initial exposure to the pressure corresponding to the upper limit of the scale error test prescribed in subparagraph (i); and while the altimeter is at this pressure, the hysteresis test shall commence. Pressure shall be increased at a rate simulating a descent in altitude at the rate of 5,000 to 20,000 feet per minute until within 3,000 feet of the first test point (50 percent of maximum altitude). The test point shall then be approached at a rate of approximately 3,000 feet per minute. The altimeter shall be kept at this pressure for at least 5 minutes, but not more than 15 minutes, before the test reading is taken. After the reading has been taken, the pressure shall be increased further, in the same manner as before, until the pressure corresponding to the second test point (40 percent of maximum altitude) is reached. The altimeter shall be kept at this pressure for at least one minute, but not more than 10 minutes, before the test reading is taken. After the reading has been taken, the pressure shall be increased further, in the same manner as before, until atmospheric pressure is reached. The reading of the altimeter at either of the two test points shall not differ by more than the tolerance specified in Table II from the reading of the altimeter for the corresponding altitude recorded during the scale error test prescribed in subparagraph (i).

(iii) *After effect*—Not more than 5 minutes after the completion of the hysteresis test prescribed in subparagraph (ii), the reading of the altimeter (corrected for any change in atmospheric pressure) shall not differ from the original atmospheric pressure reading by more than the tolerance specified in Table II.

(iv) *Friction*—The altimeter shall be subjected to a steady rate of decrease of pressure approximating 750 feet per minute. At each altitude listed in Table III, the change in reading of the pointers after vibration shall not exceed the corresponding tolerance listed in Table III.

(v) *Case leak*—The leakage of the altimeter case, when the pressure within it corresponds to an altitude of 18,000 feet, shall not change the altimeter reading by more than the tolerance shown in Table II during an interval of one minute.

(vi) *Barometric scale error*—At constant atmospheric pressure, the barometric pressure scale shall be set at each of the pressures (falling within its range of adjustment) that are listed in Table IV, and shall cause the pointer to indicate the equivalent altitude difference shown in Table IV with a tolerance of 25 feet.

(2) Altimeters which are the air data computer type with associated computing systems, or which incorporate air data correction internally, may be tested in a manner and to specifications developed by the manufacturer which are acceptable to the Administrator.

[(c) Automatic Pressure Altitude Reporting Equipment and ATC Transponder System Integration Test. The test must be conducted by an appropriately rated person under the conditions specified in paragraph (a). Measure the automatic pressure altitude at the output of the installed ATC transponder when interrogated on Mode C at a sufficient number of test points to ensure that the altitude reporting equipment, altimeters, and ATC transponders perform their intended functions as installed in the aircraft. The difference between the automatic reporting output and the altitude displayed at the altimeter shall not exceed 125 feet.]

[(d)] Records: Comply with the provisions of § 43.9 of this chapter as to content, form and disposition of the records. The person performing the altimeter tests shall record on the altimeter the date and maximum altitude to which the altimeter has been tested and the persons approving the airplane for return to service shall enter that data in the airplane log or other permanent record.

TABLE I

Altitude (Feet)	Equivalent pressure (inches of mercury)	Tolerance ±(Feet)
−1,000	31.018	20
0	29.921	20
500	29.385	20
1,000	28.856	20
1,500	28.335	25
2,000	27.821	30
3,000	26.817	30
4,000	25.842	35
6,000	23.978	40
8,000	22.225	60
10,000	20.577	80
12,000	19.029	90
14,000	17.577	100
16,000	16.216	110
18,000	14.942	120
20,000	13.750	130
22,000	12.636	140
25,000	11.104	155
30,000	8.885	180
35,000	7.041	205
40,000	5.538	230
45,000	4.355	255
50,000	3.425	280

TABLE II—TEST TOLERANCES

Test	Tolerance (Feet)
Case Leak Test	± 100
Hysteresis Test:	
First Test Point (50 percent of maximum altitude)	75
Second Test Point (40 percent of maximum altitude)	75
After Effect Test	30

TABLE III—FRICTION

Altitude (Feet)	Tolerance (Feet)
1,000	±70
2,000	70
3,000	70
5,000	70
10,000	80
15,000	90
20,000	100
25,000	120
30,000	140
35,000	160
40,000	180
50,000	250

Table IV—PRESSURE–ALTITUDE DIFFERENCE

Pressure (Inches of Hg)	Altitude Difference (Feet)
28.10	−1727
28.50	−1340
29.00	−863
29.50	−392
29.92	0
30.50	+531
30.90	+893
30.99	+974

Appendix F

ATC Transponder Tests and Inspections

[The ATC transponder tests required by § 91.177 of this chapter may be conducted using a bench check or portable test equipment and must meet the requirements prescribed in paragraphs (a) through (d) of this Appendix. If portable test equipment with appropriate coupling to the aircraft antenna system is used, operate the test equipment at a nominal rate of 235 interrogations per second to avoid possible ATCRBS interference. An additional 3db loss is allowed to compensate for antenna coupling errors during receiver sensitivity measurements conducted in accordance with paragraph (c) (1) when using portable test equipment.

[(a) For reply radio frequency, interrogate the transponder and verify that the reply frequency of the system is 1090 ±3 MHZ.

[(b) Suppression: When the transponder is interrogated on Mode 3/A at an interrogation rate between 230 and 1000 interrogations per second for Class 1B and 2B transponders or between 230 and 1200 interrogations per second for Class 1A and 2A transponders:

[(1) Verify that the transponder does not respond to more than 1 percent of the interrogations when the amplitude of P_2 pulse is equal to the P_1 pulse.

[(2) Verify that the transponder replies to at least 90 percent of the interrogations when the amplitude of the P_2 pulse is 9db less than P_1 pulse.

[If the test is conducted with a radiated test signal, the interrogation rate shall be 235 ±5 interrogations per second unless a higher rate has been approved for the test equipment used at that location.]

(c) Receiver sensitivity:

(1) Verify that receiver sensitivity of the system is −73±4dbm by use of a test set—

(i) Connected to the antenna end of the transmission line;

(ii) Connected to the antenna terminal of the transponder with a correction for transmission line loss; or

(iii) Utilizing a radiated signal.

(2) Verify that the difference in mode 3/A and mode C receiver sensitivity does not exceed 1db.

(d) Records:

Comply with the provisions of § 43.9 of this chapter as to content, form, and disposition of the records.

Special Federal Aviation Regulation 27-5

Fuel Venting and Exhaust Emission Requirements For Turbine Engine Powered Airplanes: Compliance with Revised EPA Emission Standards and Test Procedures

Adopted: December 8, 1983 **Effective: January 1, 1984**

(Published in 48 FR 56735, December 23, 1983)

SUMMARY: This amendment to the FAA airplane emissions rule is necessary because of the revised requirements of 40 CFR Part 87, Control of Air Pollution from Aircraft and Aircraft Engines; Emission Standards and Test Procedures as amended effective January 31, 1983 (47 FR 58462). 40 CFR Part 87 includes new exhaust emission requirements for all aircraft engines manufactured on or after January 1, 1984. This amendment is in accordance with section 232 of the Clean Air Act, as amended, (42 USC § 7401) and the authority delegated to the Administrator of the FAA by the Secretary of Transportation.

COMPLIANCE—January 1, 1984 or as noted. The Director of the FEDERAL REGISTER approved the incorporation by reference of the compliance procedures set forth in Appendices 2 through 6 of ICAO ANNEX 16 Volume II—Aircraft Engine Emissions, dated February 18, 1982, effective January 1, 1984.

FOR FURTHER INFORMATION CONTACT:

Nicholas P. Krull, Air Quality Division (AEE-300), Office of Environment and Energy, Federal Aviation Administration, 800 Independence Avenue, SW, Washington, D.C. 20591, telephone (202) 755-1851).

SUPPLEMENTARY INFORMATION:

HISTORY

Under section 232 of the Clean Air Act of 1970, as amended, (the Act) (42 USC § 7401), the FAA has a duty to issue regulations that ensure compliance with all aircraft emission standards promulgated by the EPA pursuant to section 231 of the Act. The EPA aircraft emission standards are currently prescribed in EPA Regulations Part 87 (40 CFR Part 87), originally issued on July 6, 1973, and published in the Federal Register (38 FR 19088) on July 17, 1973.

Pursuant to § 232 of the Act, on December 26, 1973, the FAA issued Special Federal Aviation Regulation (SFAR) 27 (38 FR 35437; December 28, 1973). The purpose of SFAR 27 was to ensure compliance with aircraft and aircraft engine emission standards and test procedures issued by the EPA in 40 CFR Part 87.

SFAR 27, as originally issued, governed compliance with only those standards and procedures in EPA Part 87 that were to become effective on February 1, 1974. On December 23, 1974, the FAA issued SFAR 27-1 (39 FR 45008; December 30, 1974) to require compliance with the fuel venting emission standards in EPA Part 87 that became effective on January 1, 1975. SFAR 27-2, effective January 1, 1976 (40 FR 55311; November 28, 1975), governs compliance with smoke emissions standards in EPA's Part 87 applicable to new and in-use aircraft turbofan or turbojet engines with a rated power of 29,000 pounds thrust or greater, that are designed for installation and operation on subsonic airplanes. SFAR 27-3, effective January 1, 1978 (42 FR 64876; December 29, 1977) regulates compliance of JT3D engines manufactured on and after January 1, 1978, with smoke emissions standards in EPA's Part 87. Finally, SFAR 27-4, effective December 1, 1980 (45 FR 71960; October 30 1980), was issued to require phased compliance of in-use JT3D engines beginning on January 1, 1981, with total compliance required by January 1, 1985. Pursuant to § 3(b) of SFAR 27, the requirement for compliance of in-use JT3D engines was automatically deleted when the EPA deleted the requirement from 40 CFR Part 87 (48 FR 2716; January 20, 1983).

On December 30, 1982, the EPA completed rulemaking which revised 40 CFR Part 87 and republished the rule in its entirety (47 FR 58462; December 30, 1982). The revised rule contains a number of changes in definitions as well as new standards for smoke and unburned hydrocarbon emissions. The compliance date for the new smoke and unburned hydrocarbon emission standards has been scheduled to take effect January 1, 1984. On September 23, 1983, the FAA issued Notice No. 83-12 (48 FR 43637; September 23, 1983), which proposed a revised SFAR 27-5 to include the new requirements of 40 CFR Part 87. The comment period closed on October 24, 1983. A number of comments were received and they are discussed below along with the discussion of the amendment.

DISCUSSION OF THE AMENDMENT

Overview

When the EPA originally issued 40 CFR Part 87, in 1973, it was recognized that some portion of the standards could be implemented in a very short time period while other portions would require a much longer time period for development and testing. Accordingly, the FAA proceeded to promulgate enforcement regulations for the near term requirements in the form of a Special Federal Aviation Regulation, SFAR No. 27. Since that time, the EPA has recognized that some of the longer term requirements were either unneeded or practically unattainable. Those longer term requirements, originally scheduled to become effective in 1978, have been delayed until January 1, 1984, and have been extensively revised. Revised regulation 40 CFR Part 87 now contains all of the standards and the last of the effectivity dates for implementation. Pursuant to section 232 of the Clean Air Act, as amended, the FAA is required to promulgate enforcement regulations for all of the standards in 40 CFR Part 87. Therefore, this amendment is consistent with the EPA revisions to 40 CFR Part 87 and FAA's statutory duty under the Clean Air Act.

Deletion of specific reference to previous findings of compliance

SFAR 27 contained specific references to manufacturer's service bulletins containing instructions for modifications which, if incorporated in engines, constituted satisfactory evidence of compliance with 40 CFR Part 87. The references also included engine model designations which had previously been found to comply with the smoke standards of 40 CFR Part 87. That list had become long and required frequent updating as new engine models were found to demonstrate compliance with the standards. As revised, 40 CFR Part 87 contains new and in some cases more stringent standards for all turbojet and turboprop engines manufactured after January 1, 1984. The listing of all of these model designations would become cumbersome and impractical requiring frequent revision of the Federal Aviation Regulations. The FAA now deletes those specific references and instead, SFAR 27-5 states that "All methods of demonstrating compliance and all model designations previously having been found acceptable to the Administrator of the FAA shall be deemed to continue to be an acceptable demonstration of compliance with the specific standards for which they were approved."

Practical interpretation of the requirement for total compliance

The standards established by the EPA are applicable to each engine of the types and upon the dates specified in 40 CFR Part 87. Taken literally this would require that every engine to which the standards apply must demonstrate compliance with the standards. This construction would require testing each and every engine manufactured on or after January 1, 1984, unless specifically exempted. The EPA recognized in the preamble to 40 CFR Part 87, and specifically in § 87.89, that exhaust emission compliance testing of every engine would be excessively costly and accepted the need to substitute a preproduction certification program in place of extensive testing of all newly produced and in service engines. Section 87.89 has delegated the definition of this substitute certification program to the FAA with the proviso that the FAA establish the level of confidence required, provide a practical interpretation of the requirement for total compliance, establish a testing program to ensure compliance, and obtain the approval of the Administrator of the EPA prior to January 1, 1984. Consistent with EPA's position regarding compliance verification (47 FR 58469), the FAA understands that this compliance verification policy is applicable to all of the standards in 40 CFR Part 87. It should be clearly understood that any substitute certification program must have the concurrence of the Administrator of the EPA.

In developing the United States position on the International Civil Aviation Organization (ICAO) Standards and Recommended Practices for Aircraft Engine Emissions, the FAA consulted extensively with the EPA on acceptable practical interpretations of a requirement for total compliance and a testing program to ensure compliance. At that time the EPA indicated that the minimum acceptable levels would be 90% confidence that 95% of the engines would meet the gaseous emission standards and a 90% confidence that every engine would meet the smoke standards. ICAO adopted such a compliance procedure based upon a composite analysis of historic engine to engine variabilities. Since the EPA has stressed the desirability of maintaining commonality with ICAO, the FAA adopts the compliance procedure defined in Appendix 6 to ICAO Annex 16 Volume II—Aircraft Engine Emissions, dated February 18, 1982. The Administrator of the EPA has concurred in FAA adoption of the ICAO compliance procedure. The FAA continues to solicit recommendations for equivalent procedures and will give each recommendation full consideration if it is accompanied by substantive supporting data. Should an equivalent or better procedure be received, the FAA will seek EPA concurrence with that as an alternate compliance procedure. The FAA cannot, however, adopt any proposed compliance procedure unless it has the concurrence of the Administrator of the EPA.

Comments in response to Notice 83-12

A total of seven written and three oral comments were received in response to Notice 83-12. The majority of those comments concerned the alleged redundancy of the regulation, the marking and identification requirements, and the exemption and reporting procedures. At least two comments indicated some continuing confusion over the definition of the term "date of manufacture". All of the comments have been reviewed and, as discussed below, the proposed rule has been revised to reflect meritorious comments and suggestions within the scope of Notice 83-12.

Redundancy of the proposed compliance requirements

One commenter noted that the proposed rule imposes compliance requirements upon the engine manufacturer, installers of engines, aircraft manufacturers, and airplane operators. The commenter felt that compliance need only be the responsibility of the engine manufacturer. From a legal viewpoint, the Clean Air Act requires that the regulations "shall include provisions making such standards applicable in the issuance, amendment, modification, suspension, or revocation of *any* certificate authorized by the Federal Aviation Act or the Department of Transportation Act." (42 USC 7572(a), *emphasis added*). From a practical and legal viewpoint, the engine manufacturer can only maintain control over the engines while they are in his possession. Yet, situations may arise where compliance may subsequently be required. For example, an engine originally manufactured and sold for export may be exempt from the standards but that same engine may not be exempt if it is resold for use in the United States as a civil aircraft engine. In that event, it would no longer be the manufacturer's responsibility to ensure compliance but rather the operator or the new owner. Similarly, an engine originally sold by a manufacturer for use in general aviation is not subject to the unburned hydrocarbon standard. However, that standard is applicable if the rated output exceeds 26.7 kilonewtons and the engine is installed and operated in the U.S. by an air carrier or a commercial operator. For these and other reasons, it is necessary to impose compliance requirements upon airplane operators, mechanics, and aircraft manufacturers, as well as the engine manufacturer. It also explains the justification for requiring that the engine exhaust emission compliance status be clearly and permanently identified in a prominent location on each powerplant.

Exemption Requirements

As stated in Notice 83-12, the EPA has retained primary rulemaking authority over the emissions standards, and the test procedures for control of those standards, in all aircraft. However, under the revised Part 87, responsibility for initial evaluation and processing of requests for certain specified exemptions has been transferred to the Secretary of the Department of Transportation (DOT). Several exemptions listed at 40 CFR § 87.7 clearly fall within the discretion of the FAA and EPA and therefore can only be considered by utilizing the procedural requirements of 14 CFR Part 11. These exemptions include 40 CFR § 87.7(a) (4), § 87.7(c), and § 87.7(d). However, several commenters have asked if it was the FAA's intent to require a formal exemption request for the remainder of the exemptions listed under 40 CFR § 87.7. To make the requirements clear, each of the remaining exemptions will be discussed in turn.

40 CFR § 87.7(a) (1) establishes an exemption for engines installed on an aircraft intended for export. The FAA has an obligation to ensure that exported engines not in compliance with the emission requirements are not operated in the United States. With this objective in mind, the FAA has determined that the marking and recording requirements discussed below, together with the existing Part 21, Subpart L requirements for Export Airworthiness Approvals, will ensure that exported engines cannot be returned for use in the United States without emission modification to bring them into compliance with SFAR 27. Accordingly, the final rule has been amended to require that any engine manufactured under the provisions of 40 CFR § 87.7(a) (1) for export on or after January 1, 1984, must have marked upon the engine manufacturer's identification plate (I.D. plate) the designator NON-US. In addition, the permanent powerplant record (engine logbook or equivalent document) must note that the exempt engine is not suitable for operation within the United States. Finally, when the exempt engine is installed in an aircraft, the aircraft's logbook must note that the aircraft "may not be operated within the United States." This notation may be removed if the engine is later modified to comply with 40 CFR Part 87, or becomes specifically exempted from the applicable emission requirements. These changes are necessary to avoid requiring engine manufacturers to obtain a formal exemption or report the serial number of engines intended for export. The later requirement would be duplicative and unnecessary in light of current regulation and policy.

40 CFR § 87.7(a) (2) permits non complying engines to be flown for short durations to a base where maintenance can be performed, to a point of storage, of for the purpose of returning an aircraft to service. Since § 87.7(a) (2) in effect establishes an applicability criteria for Part 87, the FAA does not feel that the procedural requirements of 14 CFR Part 11 must be followed in order to legally conduct this type of operation. Instead of requiring an operator to "petition" for a nondiscretionary exemption, the FAA recognizes a need for prior notification of intent to conduct such operations. Therefore, though the procedural requirements of 14 CFR Part 11 need not be followed, prior FAA authorization is required. Since the FAA views this type of operation as analogous to those requiring a special flight permit, to obtain such authorization, the operator should follow the procedures outlines in 14 CFR § 21.199.

40 CFR § 87.7(a) (3) allows for flights of short duration at infrequent intervals if conducted as part of an official visit by representatives of foreign governments. After careful consideration, the FAA has determined that the infrequency of these types of operations does not warrant prior FAA approval of any sort. Therefore, no additional FAA approval is necessary if the flight is indeed of limited duration and is conducted exclusively for the purpose of an official foreign visit.

40 CFR § 87.7(b) provides for an exemption for engines operated in the United States when certain low production limits are maintained. The FAA has an obligation to ensure that the low production limits of 40 CFR § 87.7(b) are not exceeded. The only adequate method to ensure compliance with the low production limits is to require a formal exemption request. Consequently, each time a manufacturer intends to use or sell a non complying engine in the United States, a request for exemption utilizing the procedural requirements of 14 CFR Part 11 must be made. To implement this procedure, a manufacturer should request an exemption for any group of 20 or less engines that a manufacturer intends to produce under a given type certificate during a given calendar year. Assuming that there are no irregularities, the FAA will grant the exemption on condition that the manufacturer advise the FAA of that engine's serial number and type certificate number on or before the last day of the month following the date of its manufacture. In addition, as will be explained later, that engine must be labelled as EXEMPT at FAA Headquarters which will contain the serial number of the engine as part of each exemption. At the same time, the manufacturer must note in the permanent powerplant record that the engine is not required to meet the emissions standards of 40 CFR Part 87 by reason of the low production exemption. In a related issue, several commenters have stated that it is impossible to project the market for specified engines in advance of the manufacture date and therefore it is unreasonable to require manufacturers to advise the FAA of exempted engines "on or before the date of manufacture" as proposed in Section 9(c). The FAA agrees with these commenters and has revised the final rule to provide relief in several ways. First, as adopted, the final rule requires that a manufacturer advise the FAA of the serial numbers of only those engines which have been granted a specific exemption pursuant to 14 CFR Part 11. In addition, the manufacturer may wait until the last day of the month following the date of the engine's manufacture to provide the FAA with this information.

Date of Manufacture

Although the identical definition has been part of SFAR–27 for some time, several comments were received which indicate that the term "Date of Manufacture", was misunderstood or subject to misinterpretation. One commenter expressed a desire to interpret "date of manufacture" as the date of installation on an airplane or even the date of sale of that aircraft. A second commenter expressed concern that engines in transport from the engine manufacturer to an airframe manufacturer (or in inventory at a general aviation facility) on January 1, 1984, would be subject to the revised 40 CFR Part 87 requirements. Both interpretations are too broad. The meaning of the term "Date of Manufacture" was extensively discussed in the preamble to SFAR 27–3 adopted December 21, 1977, and remains unchanged. However, to further clarify, the date on which an engine is "manufactured" is the date on which the engine is originally approved by the FAA. An engine is considered to be approved by the FAA when it is produced under an FAA Production Certificate issued under the provisions of 14 CFR Part 21, Subpart G, or under a Type Certificate Only issued under the provisions of 14 CFR Part 21, Subpart F. In addition, the engine must have been determined by the manufacturer to be in conformity with its type design and in a condition for safe operation in accordance with 14 CFR § 21.165 or § 21.130 as appropriate. Evidence of this approval is the manufacturer's fire proof identification (I.D.) plate that must be affixed to the engine in accordance with 14 CFR § 45.11 and § 45.13. In the case of a foreign manufactured engine, the "date of manufacture" is the date when the certificating authority of the country of manufacture issues a certifying statement to the effect that the engine conforms to its U.S. type design and is in a condition for safe operation.

Notice 83–12 proposed that the date of manufacture be included on the I.D. plate as part of the engine identification data. Several commenters have alleged that this requirement is redundant since the same information must be included as part of the permanent powerplant record that accompanies the engine, and because the date of manufacture is directly traceable to the engine serial number. Obviously, knowledge of the date of manufacture is essential to the FAA inspector who must determine whether the revised requirements of 40 CFR Part 87 are applicable to the engine. For an engine with a long maintenance history, specific items of information may be difficult and time consuming to locate. In addition, since there is currently no requirement that serial numbers be reported to the FAA, no master list exists for an inspector to consult. In any event, an inspector should not be required to examine additional records to determine if a particular engine must comply with revised 40 CFR Part 87. It is therefore, the FAA's position that the only efficient method of determining whether a particular engine falls within the requirements of 40 CFR Part 87 is to have the date of manufacture indicated on the I.D. plate of each particular engine. The FAA also wishes to make clear that only those engines manufactured on or after January 1, 1984, covered by the applicable provisions of 40 CFR Part 87 will be required to include the date of manufacture as part of the identification data of the engine I.D. plate. This can be done simply by indicating the month and year in a clear and concise fashion. As an example, the FAA suggests a designation such as "01–84" be marked on the I.D. plate to indicate a manufacturing date of January, 1984, as a means of complying with the "date of manufacture" requirement. The FAA is aware of several manufacturers who already routinely include this information on the engine I.D. plate. Therefore, it should not be unduly burdensome to now require this information.

Another comment regarding the date of manufacture requirement was that such a date may be confusing and misleading to potential buyers of used engines. The commenter asserted that, as an example, a 15 year old engine may have had substantial service and parts replacement by the year 1999, leaving only the I.D. plate of 1984 vintage. However, this same commenter admitted that the date of manufacture, as well as data on major maintenance actions, parts replacement, and service bulletin compliance, is already included in the engine logbook which is required for each engine. Therefore, potential buyers of the engine should not be confused as to the engine's serviceability. Rather, the date of manufacture should help to clarify what maintenance and parts are required to keep in compliance with SFAR–27.

Identification Data and Recording Requirements

In addition to the date of manufacture, proposed Section 20 of Notice 83–12 requires that the I.D. plate show a designation that indicates the status of compliance with the applicable provisions of 40 CFR Part 87. Several commenters have asked what type of indication the FAA will require. They are concerned that some I.D. plates may have to be redesigned, thus adding to the cost of production, if additional I.D. plate information data is required. After careful consideration of this problem, the FAA has devised the following 6 character marking scheme which should cover all possible marking problems that may be encountered and at the same time minimize the use of space on plates already being utilized. For engines that, in all respects, comply with the requirements of SFAR–27 and 40 CFR Part 87, the I.D. plate must contain the designation COMPLY. Any engines subject to SFAR–27, but which has been granted an exemption under any provision found in 40 CFR § 87.7(a) (4), § 87.7(b), (c) or (d), must contain the designator EXEMPT on the I.D. plate. Finally, any engine which is exempt from the requirements of SFAR–27 by reason of it being manufactured for use outside the United States [40 CFR § 87.7(a) (1)], the I.D. plate must be marked with the designator NON-US. These designations have been approved by the FAA and have been made part of Section 20 in the final rule. Other designation codes are possible for use. However, in order to retain as uniform a marking scheme as possible, only those designators approved by the Administrator of the FAA may be utilized.

Several additional recording requirements have also been included in Section 20 of the final rule. Section 20(c) requires that, for any engine which has been granted an exemption by reason of any provision found in 40 CFR § 87.7(a) (1), (a) (4), (b), (c), or (d), an indication of the exemption and the reason for the grant must be inserted in the permanent powerplant record (engine logbook or equivalent document), that accompanies the engine, at the time of manufacture. For example, if an engine has been granted an exemption by reason of it falling within the low production limits of 40 CFR § 87.7(b), the indication should state "EXEMPT for low production" or some similar notation. If an engine has been granted an exemption by reason of 40 CFR § 87.7(a) (1), the indication should read "NON-US, this engine does not comply with U.S. emissions requirements and must not be operated within the U.S."

Section 20(d) requires that, for engines rated in excess of 26.7 kilonewtons (Kn) that comply only with the required smoke number, the notation "May not be used as a commercial aircraft engine", as that term is defined in the SFAR 27-5, must be inserted in the permanent powerplant record at the time of engine manufacture. However, the I.D. plate designator COMPLY would be appropriate for these engines.

Finally, as previously mentioned, for aircraft assembled with engines exempt as a result of the export provision of 40 CFR § 87.7(a) (1), the notation "The aircraft may not be operated within the United States" must be inserted in the aircraft logbook at the time of engine installation. Other notations may be acceptable if prior FAA approval is obtained.

Stay of Emission Requirements for Class TF Engines

Subsequent to the publication of final rule 40 CFR Part 87, the General Aviation Manufacturers Association (GAMA) petitioned the Environmental Protection Agency for reconsideration of the smoke standard as applied to Class TF engines rated at 26.7 kn or below. Pursuant to an agreement between the parties, EPA has stayed the effectiveness of the smoke standard as applied to Class TF engines (48 FR 46481) October 12, 1983). The FAA has no way of knowing when or if EPA will lift this stay after reconsideration of the GAMA petition. Therefore, consistent with Section 3(b) of SFAR 27-5, the FAA will not enforce any additional requirements set forth in the final rule with respect to these engines while the stay is in effect. However, compliance with those requirements currently in effect will continue to be required. In addition, should EPA decide to reimpose any requirement previously imposed in 40 CFR Part 87, it will immediately become part of this rule.

Regulatory Impact Analysis

Prior to its enactment, the EPA determined that 40 CFR Part 87 would not constitute a major rule as defined by Executive Order 12291 (Order) and that it did not involve any significant increased costs or adverse effects on competition, employment, investment, productivity, innovation, or the ability of U.S. enterprises to compete with those of other countries when compared to the present regulations. The information base, including the economic analyses on which this determination was made, is collected in Public Docket No. OMSAPC-78-1 at the Environmental Protection Agency, Central Docket Section, West Tower Lobby, Gallery I, 401 M Street, S.W., Washington, D.C. 20460. In addition, several of the final EPA reports concerning this subject can be found as part of the docket for this proposed rule. As the purpose of the proposed amendments to SFAR 27 is to promulgate rules for the enforcement of revised 40 CFR Part 87, as required by statute, the FAA has made a determination that an additional analysis would, at this point, be duplicate and inappropriate. As a result, no new economic analysis will be conducted with regard to revised SFAR 27.

Impact on Small Entities

Because of the limited classes of engines to which 40 CFR Part 87 applies, the EPA earlier determined that enactment of that regulation would not have a significant economic impact on a substantial number of small entities (as defined by the Small Business Act). Therefore, no Regulatory Flexibility Analysis was prepared. Interested persons may review the information on which this determination was made at the locations previously mentioned. As the EPA is in a much better position to make a determination in that regard, the FAA adopts that finding.

Environmental Analysis

Pursuant to Department of Transportation, "Policies and Procedures for Considering Environmental Impacts" (FAA Order 1050.1C, Appendix 7, paragraph 5a.; 45 FR 2279, 2280, January 10, 1980), the FAA is categorically excluded from providing an environmental analysis with regard to the proposed amendments to SFAR 27 because it is mandated by law to issue regulations to ensure compliance with the EPA aircraft emissions standards and the EPA has performed all required environmental analyses prior to the issuance of those standards.

OMB Review

This action was submitted to the Office of Management and Budget for review as required by Executive Order 12291.

Good Cause Justification

Section 553 of the Administrative Procedure Act provides that the publication of a substantive rule shall be made not less than 30 days before its effective date except as otherwise provided by the agency for good cause found and published with the final rule. The EPA published the revised requirement of 40 CFR Part 87 on December 30, 1982. At that time, EPA announced a compliance date for the revised requirements of January 1, 1984. As previously stated, the FAA has a duty to issue regulations that ensure compliance with all aircraft emission standards. The amendments to SFAR 27 were published in notice form and the comments relating to that notice have been addressed. Inasmuch as the amendments to SFAR 27 are mainly procedural and the compliance date for CFR Part 87 was announced 13 months in advance, the FAA feels that there is good cause to dispense with the full 30-day publication period before the effectivity of SFAR 27-5.

Paperwork Reduction Act

Information collection requirements contained in this regulation (sections 9d, 12 and 20) have been approved by the Office of Management and Budget under the provisions of the Paperwork Reduction Act of 1980 (P.L. 96-511) and have been assigned OMB control number 2120-0508.

Accordingly, SFAR 27 of Title 14, Parts 11, 21, 43, 45, and 91 of the Code of Federal Regulations is revised and approved by the Office of Management and Budget under OMB control number 2120-0508, and § 11.101(b) of Subpart F is amended effective January 1, 1984.

NOTE: For reasons discussed earlier in the preamble: the FAA has determined that this document; (1) involves a proposed regulation which is not major under Executive Order 12291; (2) is not a significant rule pursuant to the Department of Transportation Regulatory Policies and Procedures (44 FR 11034; February 26, 1979); and (3) it is certified under the criteria of the Regulatory Flexibility Act that this rule will not have a significant economic impact on a substantial number of small entities.

(Sec. 232, Clean Air Act, as amended Dec. 31, 1970, Pub. L. 91-604 (42 U.S.C. 1857f-10) as delegated (36 FR 3733); 40 CFR Part 87; secs. 307(c), 313(a), 601 and 603, Federal Aviation Act of 1958 (49 U.S.C. 1348(c), 1354(a), 1421, and 1423); 49 U.S.C. 106(g) (Revised, Pub. L. 97-449, January 12, 1983)).

Special Federal Aviation Regulation 27

Fuel Venting and Exhaust Emission Requirements For Turbine Engine Powered Airplanes

[Sec. 1 General requirements.

(a) This SFAR provides for the approval or acceptance by the Administrator of the FAA for the Administrator of the EPA of testing and sampling methods, analytical techniques, and related equipment not identical to those specified in this Part. Before either approves or accepts any such alternate, equivalent, or otherwise nonidentical procedures or equipment, the Administrator of the FAA or the Administrator of the EPA shall consult with the other in determining whether or not the action requires rulemaking under sections 231 and 232 of the Clean Air Act, as amended, consistent with the responsibilities of the Administrator of the EPA and the Secretary of Transportation under sections 231 and 232 of the Act. (42 U.S.C. 7571, 7572).

(b) U.S. airplanes. This SFAR applies to civil airplanes that are powered by aircraft gas turbine engines of the classes specified herein and that have U.S. Standard Airworthiness Certificates.

(c) Foreign airplanes. Pursuant to the definition of "aircraft" in 40 CFR 87.1(a), this SFAR applies to civil airplanes that are powered by aircraft gas turbine engines of the classes specified herein and that have foreign airworthiness certificates that are equivalent to U.S. Standard Airworthiness Certificates. This includes only those foreign civil airplanes that, if registered in the United States, would be required by applicable Federal Aviation Regulations to have a U.S. standard airworthiness certificate in order to conduct the operations intended for the airplane.

Pursuant to 40 CFR 87.3, this SFAR does not apply where inconsistent with an obligation assumed by the United States to a foreign country in a treaty, convention, or agreement.

Sec. 3 Relation to 40 CFR Part 87

(a) Reference in this regulation to 40 CFR Part 87 refers to Title 40 of the Code of Federal Regulations, Chapter I—Environmental Protection Agency, Part 87, Control of Air Pollution from Aircraft and Aircraft Engines (40 CFR Part 87), originally issued on July 6, 1973, and published in the Federal Register (38 FR 19088) on July 17, 1973, as revised effective January 31, 1983 (47 FR 58462), as amended effective January 20, 1983 (48 FR 2716).

(b) This SFAR contains regulations to ensure compliance with certain standards in Environmental Protection Agency (EPA), 40 CFR Part 87. If EPA takes any action, including the issuance of an exemption or issuance of a revised or alternate procedure, test method, or other regulation, the effect of which is to relax, or delay the effective date of any provision of 40 CFR Part 87 that is made applicable to an aircraft under this SFAR, the new relaxed EPA requirement, upon its effective date, is incorporated into this SFAR and supersedes the provisions of this SFAR that are based on the provisions of 40 CFR Part 87 that were relaxed by such action.

(c) Unless otherwise stated, all terminology and abbreviations in this SFAR that are defined in 40 CFR Part 87 have the meaning specified in that Part, and] [all terms in 40 CFR Part 87 that are not defined in that Part but that are used in this SFAR have the meaning given them in the Clean Air Act, as amended by 42 USC § 7401.

(d) All interpretations of 40 CFR Part 87 that are rendered by EPA also apply to this SFAR.

(e) Consistent with subsection (c) of this section, the following definitions apply:

(1) "Administrator of the FAA" means the Administrator of the Federal Aviation Administration or any other officer or employee of the Federal Aviation Administration to whom the authority involved may be delegated.

(2) "Administrator of the EPA" means the Administrator of the Environmental Protection Agency and any other officer or employee of the Environmental Protection Agency to whom the authority involved may be delegated.

Sec. 5 Additional EPA approvals and procedures

(a) If EPA, under 40 CFR 87.3(a) approves or accepts any testing and sampling procedures or methods, analytical techniques, and related equipment not identical to those specified in EPA Part 87, this SFAR requires a showing that such alternate, equivalent, or otherwise nonidentical procedures have been complied with, and that such alternate equipment was used to show compliance, unless the applicant elects to comply fully with 40 CFR Part 87.

(b) If the Administrator of the EPA after consultation with the Administrator of the FAA, prescribes special test procedures for any aircraft or aircraft engine that is not susceptible to satisfactory testing by the procedures in 40 CFR Part 87, this SFAR requires a showing that those special test procedures have been complied with.

(c) Wherever 40 CFR Part 87 requires agreement, acceptance, or approval by the Administrator of EPA, this SFAR requires a showing that such agreement or approval has been obtained.

Sec. 7 Relation to State and local regulations

(a) Pursuant to 42 U.S.C. § 7573, no state or political subdivision thereof may adopt or attempt to enforce any standard respecting emissions of any air pollutant from any aircraft or engine thereof unless that standard is identical to a standard made applicable to the aircraft by the terms of this SFAR.

(b) If EPA, by regulation or exemption, relaxes a provision of 40 CFR Part 87, no state or political subdivision thereof may adopt or attempt to enforce the terms of this SFAR that are superseded by the relaxed requirement.

(c) Consistent with § 87.6 of 40 CFR Part 87, if the Administrator of the FAA determines that any emission control regulation cannot be safely applied to an aircraft, that provision may not be adopted or enforced against that aircraft by a state or political subdivision thereof, even if it is in this SFAR.

(d) If any provision of this SFAR is rendered inapplicable to a foreign aircraft as provided in 40 CFR 87.3(c) and section 1(b) of this SFAR, that] [provision may not be adopted or enforced against that foreign aircraft by a state or political subdivision thereof.

Sec. 9 Petitions for rulemaking and exemption

(a) Notwithstanding Part 11 of the Federal Aviation Regulations (14 CFR Part 11), all petitions for rulemaking involving either the substance of an emission standard prescribed by EPA that is incorporated in this SFAR, or the compliance date for such standard or procedure, must be submitted to EPA. Information copies of such petitions are invited by the FAA.

(b) Petitions for rulemaking or exemption involving provisions of this SFAR that do not affect the substance or the compliance date of an emission standard or test procedure that is prescribed by EPA, and petitions for exemptions under the provisions for which the EPA has specifically granted exemption authority to the Administrator of the FAA in 40 CFR 87.7(a) (4), (b), (c), and (d), are subject to Part 11 of the Federal Aviation Regulations (14 CFR Part 11).

(c) Any engine for which a petition for exemption has been granted pursuant to subsection (b) of this section must be reported to the FAA by serial number and type certificate number on or before the last day of the month following the date of manufacture as defined in section 12 of this SFAR.

(d) Notwithstanding any other requirement of 14 CFR § 45.13, an aircraft engine specifically exempted from the applicable requirements of this SFAR pursuant to subsection (b) of this section must have the designator EXEMPT, or an equivalent designator approved by the Administrator of the FAA, inscribed as part of the identification data of the engine.

(e) Exemptions granted pursuant to any provision of 40 CFR 87 or subsection (b) of this section are not transferrable to any other engine.

(f) Exemptions requested pursuant to the provisions of 40 CFR § 87.7(a) (2) must comply with the procedural requirements set forth in 14 CFR § 21.199.

Sec. 10 Incorporation by reference

(a) General. This SFAR prescribes certain standards and procedures which are not set forth in full text in the rule. On November 22, 1983, those standards and procedures were approved by the Office of the Federal Register for incorporation by reference pursuant to 5 U.S.C. 552(a) and 1 CFR Part 51.

(b) Changes to incorporated matter. Incorporated matter which is subject to subsequent change is incorporated by reference according to the specific reference and to the identification statement. Adoption of any subsequent change in incorporated matter that impacts compliance with standards and procedures is made under 14 CFR Part 11 and 1 CFR Part 51.

(c) Identification statement. The complete title or description which identifies each published matter incorporated by reference in this SFAR is as follows:

(1) ICAO Annex 16—Environmental Protection, Volume II—Aircraft Engine Emissions, Appendices 2 through 6 dated 18 February 1982. This document can be obtained from the International Civil Aviation Organization, P.O. Box 400, Succursale: Place de L'Aviation Internationale, 1000 Sherbrooke Street West, Montreal, Quebec, Canada H3A 2R2 at $3.00 per copy.

(d) Availability for inspection. A copy of each publication incorporated by reference in this SFAR is available for public inspection at the following locations:]

[(1) FAA Office of the Chief Counsel, Rules Docket, Room 916, Federal Aviation Administration Headquarters Building, 800 Independence Avenue, S.W., Washington, D.C. 20591

(2) Department of Transportation, Branch Library, Room 930, Federal Aviation Administration Headquarters Building, 800 Independence Avenue, S.W., Washington, D.C. 20591

(3) The respective offices of the Federal Aviation Administration as follows:

(i) New England Regional Office, 12 New England Executive Park, Burlington, Massachusetts 01803.

(ii) New York Aircraft Certification Office, 181 South Franklin Avenue, Room 202, Valley Stream, New York 11581.

(iii) Atlanta Aircraft Certification Office, 1075 Innerloop Road, College Park, Georgia 30337.

(iv) Chicago Aircraft Certification Office, 2300 East Devon, Des Plaines, Illinois 60018.

(v) Central Regional Office, 601 East Twelfth Street, Kansas City, Missouri 64106.

(vi) Southwest Regional Office, 4400 Blue Mound Road, Fort Worth, Texas 76101.

(vii) Denver Aircraft Certification Field Office, 10455 East 25th Avenue, Aurora, Colorado 80010.

(viii) Northwest Regional Office, 17900 Pacific Highway South, Seattle, Washington 98168.

(ix) Western Aircraft Certification Field Office, 15000 Aviation Boulevard, Hawthorne, California (Mail Address: P.O. Box 92007 Worldway Postal Center, Los Angeles, California 90009).

(x) Anchorage Aircraft Certification Field Office, 701 C. Street, Anchorage, Alaska 99513.

(xi) Honolulu Aircraft Certification Field Office, Prince Kuhio Building, 300 Ala Moana Boulevard, Room 7108, Honolulu, Hawaii (Mail Address: P.O. Box 50246, Honolulu, Hawaii 96850).

(xii) Los Angeles Aircraft Certification Office, 4334 Donald Douglas Drive, Long Beach, California 90808.

(xiii) Brussels Aircraft Certification Staff, 15 Rue de la Loi, B–1040 Brussels, Belgium.

(xiv) FAA Representative, Office of U.S. Consulate General, Avenida Presidente Wilson, 147 Rio De Janeiro, Brazil.

(4) The Office of the Federal Register, Room 8401, 1100 "L" Street, NW., Washington, D.C.

Sec. 11 Compliance with airworthiness regulations

It must be shown that the airplane meets the airworthiness regulations constituting the type certification basis of the airplane under all conditions in which compliance with this SFAR is shown.

Sec. 12 Date of manufacture

As used in this SFAR, unless 40 CFR Part 87 of the Clean Air Act, as amended, requires otherwise, the date on which an aircraft engine is] ["manufactured" is the date on which that individual engine is originally approved by the FAA, or by a foreign country of manufacture, for installation on an aircraft. Notwithstanding any other requirements of 14 CFR § 45.13, beginning January 1, 1984, the date of manufacture (month and year) must be included as part of the identification data of engines manufactured on or after that date.

Sec. 13 Engine classes and test configuration

(a) Consistent with section 3(c) of this SFAR, the following definitions in 40 CFR 87.1 apply:

(1) "Aircraft engine" means a propulsion engine which is installed in or which is manufactured for installation in an aircraft.

(2) "Class TP" means all aircraft turboprop engines.

(3) "Class TF" means all turbofan or turbojet aircraft engines except engines of Class T3, T8, and TSS.

(4) "Class T3" means all aircraft gas turbine engines of the JT3D model family.

(5) "Class T8" means all aircraft gas turbine engines of the JT8D model family.

(6) "Class TSS" means all aircraft gas turbine engines employed for propulsion of aircraft designed to operate at supersonic flight speeds.

(7) "Commercial aircraft engine" means any aircraft engine used or intended for use by an "air carrier" (including those engaged in "intrastate air transportation") or a "commercial operator" (including those engaged in "intrastate air transportation") as these terms are defined in the Federal Aviation Act and the Federal Aviation Regulations.

(8) "Commercial aircraft gas turbine engine" means a turboprop, turbofan, or turbojet commercial aircraft engine.

(b) As prescribed in 40 CFR Part 87, the complete engine as configured for final acceptance testing, including all accessories that might reasonably be expected to influence emissions to the atmosphere excluding auxiliary gearbox-mounted components required to drive aircraft systems and service air bleed, must be functional for all testing under this SFAR.

Sec. 14 Compliance

(a) Compliance with the fuel venting emissions requirements of this SFAR that apply beginning on February 1, 1974, and beginning January 1, 1975, may be shown by any means of compliance, applied to the airframe of the engine, that prevents the intentional discharge of fuel from fuel nozzle manifolds after the engines are shut down. Acceptable means of compliance include the following:

(1) Incorporation of an FAA approved system that recirculates the fuel back into the fuel system.

(2) Capping or securing the pressurization and drain valve.

(3) Manually draining the fuel from a holding tank into a container.

(b) Continued compliance with the exhaust emissions requirements of this SFAR that became effective on February 1, 1974, January 1, 1975, January 1, 1978, and January 1, 1984, for engines for which the type design has been shown to meet those requirements, is demonstrated if the engine is maintained in accordance with applicable maintenance requirements for 14 CFR Chapter I.]

[methods of demonstrating compliance and all model designations previously having been found acceptable to the Administrator of the FAA shall be deemed to continue to be an acceptable demonstration of compliance with the specific standards for which they were approved.

(c) Each applicant must allow the Administrator of the FAA to make, or witness, any test necessary to determine compliance with the applicable provisions of this SFAR.

(d) An acceptable alternative to testing every engine is described in Appendix 6 to Volume II—Aircraft Engine Emissions, of ICAO Annex 16—Environmental Protection, 18 February 1982, incorporated herein by reference as indicated in Section 10. Other methods of demonstrating compliance may be approved by the Administrator of the FAA with the concurrence of the Administrator of the EPA.

Sec. 15 Type certificates

(a) Notwithstanding Part 21 of the Federal Aviation Regulations, and irrespective of the date of application, no type certificate is issued, on and after the dates specified in subparagraphs (a) (1) through (a) (5) of this section, for the airplanes specified therein, unless:

(1) For airplanes powered by engines of Class TF, Class TP, Class T3, Class T8, or Class TSS, the airframe or engine complies with the fuel venting emissions requirements and related test procedures of 40 CFR Part 87 that became effective on February 1, 1974, and January 1, 1975;

(2) For airplanes powered by engines of Class T8, each engine complies with the exhaust emissions requirements and related test procedures of 40 CFR Part 87 that became effective on February 1, 1974;

(3) For airplanes powered by engines of Class TF that have a rated power of 29,000 pounds thrust or greater, each engine complies with the exhaust emissions requirements and related test procedures of 40 CFR Part 87 that became effective on January 1, 1976;

(4) For airplanes powered by engines of Class T3, each engine manufactured on or after January 1, 1978, complies with the exhaust emissions requirements and related test procedures of 40 CFR Part 87 that became effective on January 1, 1978; and

(5) For airplanes powered by engines of Class TP, Class TF, Class T3, Class T8, and Class TSS—each engine manufactured on or after January 1, 1984, complies with the exhaust emissions requirements and related test procedures of 40 CFR Part 87 that apply beginning January 1, 1984.

(b) Notwithstanding Part 21 of the Federal Aviation Regulations, and irrespective of the date of application, no type certificate is issued, on and after the dates specified in paragraphs (a) (2), (a) (3) and (a) (4) of this section, for an engine specified therein unless the engine complies with that subparagraph.

(c) Notwithstanding Part 21 of the Federal Aviation Regulations and irrespective of the date of application, no type certificate is issued on or after January 1, 1984, for any Class TP, Class TF, Class T3, Class T8, or Class TSS engine unless the engine complies with the exhaust emissions requirements and related test procedures of 40 CFR Part 87 that apply beginning January 1, 1984.]

[Sec. 17 Supplemental or amended type certificates

(a) Notwithstanding Part 21 of the Federal Aviation Regulations, and irrespective of the date of application, no supplemental or amended type certificate is issued on and after the dates specified in paragraphs (a) (1) through (a) (5) of this section, for the airplanes specified therein, unless:

(1) For airplanes powered by engines of Class TF, Class TP, Class T3, Class T8, or Class TSS, the airframe or engine complies with the fuel venting emissions requirements and related test procedures of 40 CFR Part 87 that became effective on February 1, 1974, and January 1, 1975;

(2) For airplanes powered by engines of Class T8, each engine complies with the exhaust emissions requirements and related test procedures of 40 CFR Part 87 that became effective on February 1, 1974;

(3) For airplanes powered by engines of Class TF that have a rated power of 29,000 pounds thrust or greater, each engine complies with the exhaust emissions requirements and related test procedures of 40 CFR Part 87 that became effective on January 1, 1976;

(4) For airplanes powered by engines of Class T3, each engine manufactured on or after January 1, 1978, complies with the exhaust emissions requirements and related test procedures of 40 CFR Part 87 that became effective on January 1, 1978; and

(5) For airplanes powered by engines of Class TP, Class TF, Class T3, Class T8, and Class TSS—each engine manufactured on or after January 1, 1984, complies with the exhaust emissions requirements and related test procedures of 40 CFR Part 87 that apply beginning January 1, 1984.

(b) Notwithstanding Part 21 of the Federal Aviation Regulations, and irrespective of the date of application, no supplemental or amended type certificate is issued, on or after the dates specified in paragraphs (a) (2), (a) (3), and (a) (4) of this section, for an engine specified therein, unless the engine complies with that paragraph.

(c) Notwithstanding Part 21 of the Federal Aviation Regulations and irrespective of the date of application, no supplemental or amended type certificate is issued on or after January 1, 1984, for any Class TP, Class TF, Class T3, Class T8, or Class TSS engine unless the engine complies with the exhaust emissions requirements and related test procedures of 40 CFR Part 87 that apply beginning January 1, 1984.

Sec. 19 Engine approvals

(a) On and after the dates specified in this paragraph, and notwithstanding Part 21 of the Federal Aviation Regulations, no original FAA approval for installation of an engine on aircraft covered by this SFAR (including FAA acceptance of an equivalent original approval issued on or before January 1, 1978, by a foreign country of manufacture) is made by the FAA:

(1) For an engine of Class T8, unless the engine complies with the exhaust emissions requirements and related test procedures of 40 CFR Part 87 that became effective on February 1, 1974;

(2) For an engine of Class TF that has a rated power of 29,000 pounds thrust or greater, unless the engine complies with the exhaust emissions requirements and related test procedures of 40 CFR Part 87 that became effective on January 1, 1976;]

[(3) For an engine of Class T3, unless each engine manufactured on or after January 1, 1978, complies with the exhaust emissions requirements and related test procedures of 40 CFR Part 87 that became effective on January 1, 1978; and

(4) For engines of Class TP, Class TF, Class T3, Class T8, or Class TSS, unless each engine manufactured on or after January 1, 1984, complies with the exhaust emissions requirements and related test procedures of 40 CFR Part 87 that apply beginning January 1, 1984.

Sec. 20 Identification Data and Recording Requirements

(a) On or after January 1, 1984, notwithstanding 14 CFR Part 45, no original FAA approval for installation of an engine on an airplane (including FAA acceptance of an equivalent original approval issued on or after January 1, 1984, by a foreign country of manufacture) is made by the FAA, for an engine covered by this SFAR unless that engine has secured to it an identification plate displaying the date of manufacture and a designation, approved by the Administrator of the FAA, that indicates compliance with applicable provisions of 40 CFR Part 87. Approved indicators include COMPLY, EXEMPT, and NON-US as appropriate.

(b) On or after January 1, 1984, notwithstanding 14 CFR Part 45, no person may secure an identification plate to any airplane engine covered by this SFAR unless that engine complies with the applicable provisions of this SFAR.

(c) On or after January 1, 1984, notwithstanding any other requirement of 14 CFR Part 43, for any engine granted an exemption pursuant to any applicable provision of 40 CFR § 87.7(a) (1), (a) (4), (b), (c), or (d), an indication of the type of exemption and the reason for the grant must be noted in the permanent powerplant record, that accompanies the engine, at the time of manufacture of the engine.

(d) On or after January 1, 1984, notwithstanding any other requirement of 14 CFR Part 43, for any engine with a rated thrust in excess of 26.7 kilonewtons which does not comply with the hydrocarbon emissions standard of 40 CFR Part 87, the statement "May not be used as a commercial aircraft engine" must be noted in the permanent powerplant record, that accompanies the engine, at the time of manufacture of the engine.

(e) On or after January 1, 1984, notwithstanding any other requirement of 14 CFR Part 43, for any aircraft assembled with an engine that has been granted an exemption pursuant to 40 CFR § 87.7(a) (1), the notation "the aircraft may not be operated within the United States", or an equivalent notation approved by the Administrator of the FAA, must be inserted in the aircraft logbook, or alternate equivalent document, at the time of installation of the engine.

Sec. 21 Standard airworthiness certificates

Notwithstanding Part 21 of the Federal Aviation Regulations, and irrespective of the date of application, no standard airworthiness certificate is issued, on and after the dates specified in paragraphs (a) through (e) of this section, for the airplanes specified therein, unless:

(a) For airplanes powered by engines of Class TP, Class TF, Class T3, Class T8, or Class TSS the airframe or engine complies with the fuel venting emissions requirement and related test procedures of 40 CFR Part 87 that became effective on February 1, 1974, and January 1, 1975;]

[(b) For airplanes powered by engines of Class T8, each engine complies with the exhaust emissions requirements and related test procedures of 40 CFR Part 87 that became effective on February 1, 1974;

(c) For airplanes powered by engines of Class TF that have a rated power of 29,000 pounds thrust or greater, each engine complies with the exhaust emissions requirements and related test procedures of 40 CFR Part 87 that became effective on January 1, 1976;

(d) For airplanes powered by engines of Class T3, each engine manufactured on or after January 1, 1978, complies with the exhaust emissions requirements and related test procedures of 40 CFR Part 87 that became effective on January 1, 1978; and

(e) For airplanes powered by engines of Class TP, Class TF, Class T3, Class T8, and Class TSS—each engine manufactured on or after January 1, 1984, complies with the exhaust emissions requirements and related test procedures of 40 CFR Part 87 that apply beginning January 1, 1984.

Sec. 25 Operation

On and after the dates specified in paragraphs (a) through (e) of this section, no person may, within the United States, operate a airplane specified in those paragraphs unless:

(a) For airplanes powered by engines of Class TP, Class TF, Class T3, Class T8, or Class TSS, the airframe or the engine complies with the fuel venting emissions requirements and related test procedures of 40 CFR Part 87 that became effective on February 1, 1974, and January 1, 1975;

(b) For airplanes powered by engines of Class T8, each engine complies with the exhaust emissions requirements and related test procedures of 40 CFR Part 87 that became effective on February 1, 1974;

(c) For airplanes powered by engines of Class TF that have a rated power of 29,000 pounds thrust or greater, each engine complies with the exhaust emissions requirements and related test procedures of 40 CFR Part 87 that became effective on January 1, 1976;

(d) For airplanes powered by engines of Class T3, each engine manufactured on or after January 1, 1978, complies with the exhaust emissions requirements and related test procedures of 40 CFR Part 87 that became effective on January 1, 1978; and

(e) For airplanes powered by engines of Class TP, Class TF, Class T3, Class T8, and Class TSS—each engine manufactured on or after January 1, 1984, complies with the exhaust emissions requirements and related test procedures of 40 CFR Part 87 that apply beginning January 1, 1984.]

Appendix III

Federal Aviation Advisory Circular 20-27 Certification and Operation of Amateur-Built Aircraft

U.S. Department of Transportation
Federal Aviation Administration

Advisory Circular

Subject: CERTIFICATION AND OPERATION OF AMATEUR-BUILT AIRCRAFT

Date: 4/1/83
Initiated by: AWS-200

AC No: 20-27C
Change:

1. PURPOSE. This advisory circular (AC) provides guidance and information relative to the airworthiness certification and operation of amateur-built aircraft.

2. CANCELLATIONS.

a. AC 20-27B, Certification and Operation of Amateur-Built Aircraft, dated April 20, 1972.

b. AC 20-28A, Nationally Advertised Construction Kits Amateur-Built Aircraft, dated December 29, 1972.

3. BACKGROUND.

a. The FAA has received many requests from amateur aircraft builders for information relative to the construction, certification, and operation of amateur-built aircraft. This AC provides guidance concerning the building, certification, and operation of amateur-built aircraft of all types; defines the eligibility of nationally advertised kits; defines how much construction the amateur builder must do to have the aircraft eligible for airworthiness certification; and describes the FAA role in the certification process.

b. The Federal Aviation Regulations (FAR) provide for the issuance of experimental certificates to permit the operation of amateur-built aircraft. FAR § 21.191(g) defines an amateur-built aircraft as an aircraft, the major portion of which has been fabricated and assembled by person(s) who undertook the construction project solely for their education or recreation. The FAA has interpreted this rule to require that more than 50 percent of the aircraft must have been fabricated and assembled by the individual or group. Commercially produced components and parts which are normally purchased for use in aircraft may be used, including engines and engine accessories, propellers, tires, spring steel landing gear, main and tail rotor blades, rotor hubs, wheel and brake assemblies, forgings, castings, extrusions, and standard aircraft hardware such as pulleys, bellcranks, rod ends, bearings, bolts, rivets, etc.

4. DEFINITION. As used herein, the term "District Office" means the FAA General Aviation (GADO), Flight Standards (FSDO), or Manufacturing Inspection (MIDO) District Office that will perform the airworthiness inspection and certification of an amateur-built aircraft.

5. FAA INSPECTION CRITERIA.

a. In the past, the FAA has inspected amateur-built aircraft at several stages during the construction of the aircraft. These inspections are commonly referred to as precover inspections. The FAA also inspected the aircraft upon completion (prior to the initial issuance of the special airworthiness certificate necessary to show compliance with FAR 91.42(b)), and again prior to the issuance of the unlimited special airworthiness certificate. In the interest of streamlining operations within the government, and utilizing FAA inspection resources in areas most affecting safety, the FAA has reassessed its position concerning the need for all of these inspections. The following reflects the results of this assessment:

(1) The amateur-built program was designed to permit any person to build and operate an aircraft solely for educational and recreational purposes. The FAA has always maintained that the amateur builder may select his/her own design and should not be inhibited by any overly stringent FAA requirements. The FAA does not approve these designs since it would not be praticable to develop design standards for the multitude of unique design configurations that are generated by amateur builders.

(2) FAA inspections of these aircraft are limited to ensuring the use of acceptable workmanship methods, techniques, and practices; verification of flight tests to ensure that the particular aircraft is controllable throughout its normal range of speeds and throughout all the maneuvers to be executed; and determination of operating limitations necessary to protect persons and property not involved in this activity.

(3) In recent years, amateur builders have adopted a practice whereby they call upon a person having expertise with aircraft construction techniques (such as Experimental Aircraft Association (EAA) designees, reference paragraph 7d(1)), to inspect particular components, e.g., wing assemblies, fuselages, etc., prior to covering, and conduct other inspections, as deemed necessary. This practice has been highly successful in ensuring construction integrity.

(4) There are many instances where the FAA has found that precover inspections were unnecessary, since in some cases the areas requiring inspection were readily accessible when the aircraft was completed. In other instances, precover inspections were found to be neither meaningful nor feasible, such as in cases involving aircraft constructed from composite materials.

(5) The FAA inspection previously performed after successful completion of the flight test, and prior to issuance of an unlimited certificate, was determined to be redundant in that any workmanship discrepancies would be detected during inspections performed prior to the issuance of the initial special airworthiness certificate.

b. In view of the foregoing considerations, the FAA has concluded that safety objectives, relative to the amateur-built program, can be best accomplished, with no derogation of safety, by the use of the following criteria:

(1) Amateur builders should continue the practice of having knowledgeable persons (i.e. EAA designees, FAA certificated mechanics, etc.) perform precover inspections and other inspections as appropriate. In addition, builders should document construction using photographs taken at appropriate times prior to covering. The photographs should clearly show methods of construction and quality of workmanship. Such photographic records should be included with the builder's log or other construction records.

(2) The FAA will conduct an inspection of the aircraft prior to the issuance of the initial special airworthiness certificate to enable the applicant to show compliance with FAR 91.42(b). This inspection will include a review of the information required by FAR 21.193, the aircraft builder's log books, and an examination of the completed aircraft to ensure that proper workmanship has been used in the construction of the aircraft. Appropriate operating limitations will also be prescribed at this time.

(3) Upon completion of the required flight test, the FAA will review the results of the tests accomplished, as recorded in the aircraft log book. Upon a determination that compliance has been shown with FAR 91.42(b), the FAA will issue the unlimited special airworthiness certificate with expanded operating limitations.

6. CERTIFICATION STEPS. The following procedures are in the general order to be followed in the certification process:

a. Initial Step. The prospective builder should contact the nearest District Office to discuss his plans for building the aircraft with an FAA inspector. During this contact, the type of aircraft, its complexity and/or materials should be discussed. The FAA will provide the prospective builder with any guidance necessary to ensure a better understanding of applicable regulations.

b. Registration. Prior to completion of the aircraft, the builder may apply for an identification number and register the aircraft. Detailed procedures are in paragraph 7a. This must be done before submitting an Application for Airworthiness Certificate, FAA Form 8130-6, under FAR § 21.173.

c. Marking. The identification number (N-number) assigned to the aircraft, and an identification plate must be affixed in accordance with FAR § 21.182 and FAR Part 45, Identification and Registration Marking. Detailed procedures are in paragraph 7b.

d. Application. The builder may apply for an experimental certificate by submitting the following documents and data to the nearest District Office:

(1) Application for Airworthiness Certificate, FAA Form 8130-6.

(2) Enough data (such as photographs) to identify the aircraft.

(3) An Aircraft Registration Certificate, AC Form 8050-3, or the pink copy of the Aircraft Registration Application, AC Form 8050-1.

(4) A statement setting forth the purpose for which the aircraft is to be used; i.e. "operating an amateur-built aircraft, FAR 21.191(g)."

(5) A notarized statement that the applicant fabricated and assembled the major portion (reference paragraph 7e) of the aircraft, for education or recreation, and has evidence to support the statement available to the FAA upon request (see Appendix 3 for sample).

(6) Evidence of inspections, such as a log book entry signed by the builder describing all inspections conducted during construction of the aircraft. This will substantiate that the construction has been accomplished in accordance with acceptable workmanship methods, techniques, and practices, in addition to photographic documentation of construction details.

e. FAA Inspection and Issuance of Airworthiness Certificate.

(1) After inspection of the documents and data submitted with the application, the FAA will inspect the aircraft, and upon a determination that the aircraft has been properly constructed will issue an experimental certificate together with operating limitations that specify the flight test area. The inspector will verify that all required markings are properly applied, including the following placard which must be displayed in the cabin or the cockpit at a location where it is in full view of all the occupants:

"PASSENGER WARNING - THIS AIRCRAFT IS AMATEUR-BUILT AND DOES NOT COMPLY WITH FEDERAL SAFETY REGULATIONS FOR STANDARD AIRCRAFT"

(2) Details concerning flight test areas are contained in paragraph 7c. The operating limitations are a part of the experimental certificate and must be displayed with the certificate when the aircraft is operated. It is the responsibility of the pilot to conduct all flights in accordance with the operating limitations, as well as the General Operating and Flight Rules in FAR Part 91.

(3) Upon satisfactory completion of operations in the assigned test area, the owner of the aircraft may apply to the FAA for amended operating limitations by submitting to the nearest District Office an Application for Airworthiness Certificate, FAA Form 8130-6. Prior to issuance of the amended limitations, the FAA inspector will review the applicant's flight log to determine whether corrective actions have been taken on any problems encountered during the testing and that aircraft condition for safe operation has been established.

7. GENERAL INFORMATION.

a. Aircraft Registration. The FAR require that all U.S. civil aircraft be registered, before an airworthiness certificate can be issued. FAR Part 47, Aircraft Registration, prescribes the requirements for registering civil aircraft. The basic procedures are as follows:

(1) Before an amateur builder can register his aircraft he must first obtain an identification number which will eventually be displayed on the aircraft. It is not necessary to obtain an identification number at an early stage in the project, especially if the builder intends to obtain a special

number of his choice. Under FAR Part 47, a special identification number costs $10.00 and may be reserved for no longer than one year. Although this reservation does not apply to numbers assigned at random by the Aircraft Registry, the best time to request identification number assignment in either case is in the later stages of construction.

(2) To apply for either a random identification number or special identification number, the owner of an amateur-built aircraft must provide information required by the FAA Aircraft Registry by completing an Affidavit of Ownership for Amateur-Built Aircraft, AC Form 8050-88. The affidavit establishes the ownership of the aircraft. If the aircraft is built from a kit, the builder should also submit a signed bill of sale from the manufacturer of the kit as evidence of ownership. Any communication sent to the FAA concerning aircraft registration should be mailed to the FAA Aircraft Registry, Department of Transportation, P.O. Box 25504, Oklahoma City, Oklahoma 73125.

(3) After receipt of the applicant's letter requesting identification number assignment, the FAA Aircraft Registry will send a form letter giving the number assignment, a blank Aircraft Registration Application, AC Form 8050-1, and other registration information. All instructions must be carefully complied with to prevent return of the application and delay in the registration process. The Aircraft Registration Application white original and green copy should be returned to the FAA Aircraft Registry within 90 days prior to the estimated completion date of the amateur-built aircraft, accompanied by a fee of $5.00 payable by check or money order to the Federal Aviation Administration. The pink copy of the application should be retained by the applicant to be carried in the aircraft as a temporary registration until the Certificate of Registration is issued.

b. Identification Marking. When a builder applies for an airworthiness certificate for his amateur-built aircraft, he must show in accordance with FAR § 21.182 that his aircraft bears the identification and registration markings required by FAR Part 45. The following summary of the pertinent rules is provided for guidance.

(1) The aircraft must be identified by means of a fireproof plate that is etched, stamped, engraved, or marked by some other approved fireproof marking as required by FAR 45.11. The identification plate must include the information required by FAR 45.13.

(2) The identification plate must be secured in such a manner that it will not likely be defaced or removed during normal service, or lost or destroyed in an accident. It must be secured to the aircraft at an accessible location near an entrance, except that if it is legible to a person on the ground it may be located externally on the fuselage near the tail surfaces.

(3) The builder's name on the data plate must be the amateur builder, not the designer, plans producer, or kit manufacturer. The model is whatever the builder wishes to assign, provided it will not be confused with other commercially built aircraft model designations.

(4) The required registration marks on most amateur-built airplanes must be displayed on either the vertical tail surfaces or the sides of the fuselage.

However, the builder should refer to FAR § 45.25, which defines specific requirements for the location of marks on fixed-wing aircraft. The location of registration marks for rotorcraft, airships, and balloons is specified in FAR § 45.27. These registration marks must be painted on or affixed by any other means insuring a similar degree of permanence. Decals are also acceptable. The use of tape which can be peeled off or water soluble paint, such as poster paint, is not considered acceptable.

(5) Most fixed-wing amateur-built aircraft are eligible to display registration marks with a minimum height of three (3) inches. However, if the maximum cruising speed of the aircraft exceeds 180 knots (207 miles per hour), registration marks at least twelve (12)inches high must be displayed. The builder should refer to FAR § 45.29, which defines the minimum size and proportions for registration marks on all types of aircraft.

(6) The identification marks displayed on the aircraft must consist of the Roman capital letter "N" (denoting United States registration) followed by the registration number of the aircraft. Any suffix letter used in the marks must also be a Roman capital letter. In addition, the word "experimental" must also be displayed on the aircraft near each entrance to the cabin or cockpit in letters not less than 2 inches nor more than 6 inches in height.

(7) If the configuration of the aircraft prevents the aircraft from being marked in compliance with any of the above requirements, the builder should contact the FAA regarding approval of a different marking procedure. It is highly recommended that any questions regarding registration marking be discussed and resolved with a local FAA Inspector before the marks are affixed to the aircraft.

c. Flight Test Areas.

(1) Amateur-built airplanes and rotorcraft will initially be limited to operation within an assigned flight test area for at least 25 hours when a type certificated (FAA-approved) engine/propeller combination is installed, or 40 hours when an uncertified (not FAA-approved) engine/propeller combination is installed. Amateur-built gliders, balloons, dirigibles and ultralight vehicles built from kits evaluated by the FAA and found eligible to meet requirements of FAR 21.191(g), for which original airworthiness certification is sought will be limited to operation within an assigned flight test area for at least 10 hours of satisfactory operation, including at least five takeoffs and landings.

(2) The desired flight test area should be requested by the applicant, and if found acceptable by the FAA Inspector will be approved and so specified in the Operating Limitations. It will usually encompass the area within a twenty-five (25) statute mile radius from the aircraft's home base. The FAA will ensure that the area selected is not over densely populated areas or in congested airways so that the flight testing, during which passengers may not be carried, would not likely impose any hazard to persons or property not involved in this activity. The shape of the flight test area selected may need to be modified to satisfy these requirements.

(3) The carrying of passengers or other crewmembers will not be permitted unless they are necessary to the conduct of the flight test while the aircraft is restricted to the flight test area.

(4) When it is shown in accordance with FAR § 91.42(b) that the aircraft is controllable throughout its normal range of speeds and all maneuvers to be executed, and has no hazardous operating characteristics or design features, and the time period in the flight test area has been completed, the owner may apply for operation outside the assigned flight test area.

d. Design and Construction.

(1) Many individuals who desire to build their own aircraft have little or no experience with respect to aeronautical practices, workmanship or design. An excellent source for advice in such matters is the Experimental Aircraft Association (EAA) located in Hales Corners, Wisconsin. The EAA is an organization established for the purpose of promoting amateur building and giving technical advice and assistance to its members. The EAA has implemented a designee program, whose aim is to ensure the safety and dependability of amateur-built aircraft. Most EAA designees are willing to inspect amateur-built aircraft projects and offer constructive advice regarding workmanship and/or design. The FAA strongly encourages the use of such designees.

(2) Any choice of engines, propellers, wheels, and other components, and any choice of materials may be used in the construction of an amateur-built aircraft. However, it is recommended that FAA-approved components and established aircraft quality material be used, especially in fabricating parts constituting the primary structure, such as wing spars, critical attachment fittings, and fuselage structural members. Inferior materials, or materials whose identity cannot be established, should not be used.

(3) The design of the cockpit or cabin of the aircraft should avoid, or provide for padding on, sharp corners or edges, protrusions, knobs and similar objects which may cause injury to the pilot or passengers in the event of an accident.

(4) An engine installation should be such that adequate fuel is supplied to the engine in all anticipated flight attitudes. Also, a suitable means, consistent with the size and complexity of the aircraft, should be provided to reduce fire hazard wherever possible, including a firewall between the engine compartment and the fuselage. When applicable, a system providing for carburetor heat should also be provided to minimize the possibility of carburetor icing.

(5) Much additional information and guidance concerning acceptable fabrication and assembly methods, techniques, and practices are provided in FAA Advisory Circular (AC) No. 43.13-1A "Acceptable Methods, Techniques, and Practices - Aircraft Inspection and Repair," and AC No. 43.13-2A, "Acceptable Methods, Techniques and Practices - Aircraft Alterations." These publications are available from the Government Printing Office.

(6) In the areas of engineering design, the builder should obtain the services of a qualified aeronautical engineer, or consult the seller of purchased plans or construction kits, as appropriate.

e. Construction Kits.

(1) Construction kits containing raw materials and some prefabricated components may be used in building an amateur-built aircraft; however, aircraft which are assembled from kits composed of completely finished prefabricated components and parts, and precut, predrilled materials are not considered to be eligible for certification as amateur-built aircraft, since the major portion of the aircraft would not have been "fabricated and assembled" by the builder.

(2) An aircraft built from a kit may be eligible for certification, provided that the major portion (more than 50 percent) has been "fabricated and assembled" by the amateur builder. The major portion of such a kit may consist of raw stock such as lengths of wood, tubing, extrusions, etc., which may have been cut to an approximate length. A certain quantity of prefrabricated parts such as heat treated ribs, bulkheads or complex forms made from sheet metal, fibre-glass, or polystyrene would also be acceptable, provided it still meets the major portion of "fabrication and assembly" requirement and the amateur builder satisfies the FAA Inspector that completion of the aircraft is not merely an assembly operation.

(3) Various material/part kits for the construction of aircraft are available nationally for use by amateur aircraft builders. Advertisements tend to be somewhat vague and may be misleading as to whether a kit is eligible for amateur-built certification. It is not advisable to order a kit prior to verifying with a FAA Inspector that the aircraft, upon completion, would be eligible for certification as amateur-built under existing rules and established policy.

(4) It should be noted that the FAA does not certify aircraft kits or approve kit manufacturers; however, the FAA does perform evaluations of kits that have potential for national sales interest, but only for the purpose of determining whether an aircraft built from the kit can meet the "major portion" criteria. Appendix 2 provides a listing of current eligible amateur aircraft kits.

f. Safety Precaution Recommendations.

(1) All Aircraft.

(a) The pilot should thoroughly familiarize himself with the ground handling characteristics of the aircraft by conducting taxi tests before attempting flight operations.

(b) Before the first flight of an amateur-built aircraft, the pilot should take precautions to ensure that emergency equipment and personnel are readily available in the event of an accident.

(c) Violent (acrobatic) maneuvers should not be attempted until sufficient flight experience has been gained to establish that the aircraft is satisfactorily controllable throughout its normal ranges of speeds and maneuvers. Those maneuvers successfully demonstrated while in the test area may continue to be permitted by the FAA when the operating limitations are expanded.

(2) Rotorcraft.

(a) The pilot should be prepared to cope with a nonconventional aircraft which has flight characteristics unlike that of an airplane.

(b) The effect of the collective pitch and cyclic pitch control movements should be thoroughly understood by the pilot.

(c) Operators of rotorcraft having fully articulated rotor systems should be particularly cautious of "ground resonance." This condition of rotor unbalance, if maintained or allowed to progress, can be extremely dangerous and usually results in structural failure.

(d) Tests showing that stability, vibration, and balance are satisfactory should normally be completed with the rotorcraft tied down, before beginning hover or horizontal flight operations.

g. Documentation Requirements.

(1) To preclude any problems or questions concerning source or specification of materials, parts, etc., used in fabricating the aircraft, it would be helpful if the builder kept copies of all invoices or other shipping documents.

(2) A construction log maintained by the builder for the project, including photographs taken as major components are completed will be acceptable substantiation that the builder constructed the major portion of the aircraft.

(3) The aircraft's flight history should be recorded in an aircraft log book. The nature as well as duration of each flight should be documented. If the aircraft is considered acrobatic, the acrobatic manuevers should be demonstrated in the flight test area and recorded in the aircraft log book.

8. RECURRENT AIRWORTHINESS CERTIFICATION. When an amateur-built aircraft has completed operations in the assigned test area, it is eligible for an UNLIMITED duration airworthiness certificate. With the issuance of the unlimited airworthiness certificate, an operating limitation requiring a condition inspection at 12 month intervals is imposed. The aircraft builder can be certified as a repairman to enable him to perform the condition inspection. Specific information regarding repairman certification can be found in AC No. 65-23, Certification of Repairmen (Experimental Aircraft Builders).

9. REFERENCE MATERIAL.

a. Federal Aviation Regulations

Part 21 - Certification Procedures for Product and Parts.
Part 45 - Identification and Registration Marking.
Part 47 - Aircraft Registration.
Part 65 - Certification: Airmen Other than Flight Crew Members.

Part 91 - General Operating and Flight Rules.
Part 101 - Moored Balloons, Kites, Unmanned Rockets, and Unmanned Free Balloons.
Part 103 - Ultralight Vehicles.

b. Advisory Circulars

20-90 - Address List for Engineering and Manufacturing District Offices (Now redesignated Manufacturing Inspection District Offices.)
*43.13-1 - Acceptable Methods, Techniques and Practices Aircraft Inspection and Repair.
*43.13-2 - Acceptable Methods, Techniques and Practices Aircraft Alterations.
65-23 - Certification of Repairmen (Experimental Aircraft Builders).
*91-23 - Pilot's Weight and Balance Handbook.

10. HOW TO GET PUBLICATIONS. The FAR and those ACs for which a fee is charged (marked with an asterisk (*) in paragraph 9(b)) may be obtained from the Superintendent of Documents, U.S. Government Printing Office, Washington, D.C. 20402. A listing of FARs and current prices is in AC 00-44, Status of Federal Aviation Regulations, and a listing of all ACs is in AC 00-2, Advisory Circular Checklist. These two ACs may be obtained free of charge from:

Department of Transportation
Publications Section, M-442.32
Washington, D.C. 20590

M. C. Beard
Director of Airworthiness

APPENDIX 1

ADDRESSES

EXPERIMENTAL AIRCRAFT ASSOCIATION, INC. (Phone: Area Code (414) 425-4860)
Mailing: P.O. Box 229
Hales Corners, Wisconsin 53130

Street: 11311 West Forest Home Avenue
Franklin, Wisconsin

FEDERAL AVIATION ADMINISTRATION
Mailing: Airmen and Aircraft Registry (Phone: Area Code (405) 686-4331)
Department of Transportation
P.O. Box 25504
Oklahoma City, Oklahoma 73125

Street: 6500 South MacArthur Boulevard
Oklahoma City, Oklahoma

PUBLICATIONS:	WRITE TO:
1. To request free advisory circulars:	U.S. Department of Transportation Publications Section, M-442.32 Washington, D.C. 20590
2. To be placed on FAA's mailing list for free advisory circulars:	U.S. Department of Transportation Distribution Requirements Section, M-481.1 Washington, D.C. 20590
3. To purchase for sale advisory circulars and FARs:	Superintendent of Documents U.S. Government Printing Office Washington, D.C. 20402

APPENDIX 2

LISTING OF ELIGIBLE AMATEUR AIRCRAFT KITS

The following is a compilation of kits that have been evaluated and found to be eligible to meet the requirements of FAR 21.191(g).

Kit Manufacturer	Model
American Eagle Light Inc. Albuquerque, New Mexico	Eagle Two Place Kit
American Eagle Corporation Muskegon, Michigan	Minibat Sailplane Kit
Birdman Aircraft Company Daytona Beach, Florida	TL-1
CGS Aviation, Incorporated Cleveland, Ohio	Hawk Model A
Christen Industries Hollister, California	Christen Eagle II Aircraft Construction Kit Array No. 1
Condor Aircraft Co. Miami, Florida	Condor III+2
DSK Aircraft Corp. Van Nuys, California	BJ-1B Duster Sailplane
Eipper-Formance, Incorporated San Marcos, California	Quicksilver MX II
Franklin Manufacturing Corporation, RD2, Landrock, Pennsylvania	Hummer Kits Model A and B
Monnet Experimental Aircraft Company Elgin, Illinois	Monerai Models Sailplane
Pitts Aerobatic Aircraft Company Afton, Wyoming	Pitts Master Kit List No. 100-200-201
Rotec Engineering, Incorporated Duncanville, Texas	Rally 3 "A"
Rotorway Incorporated Tempe, Arizona	Exec Model Helicopter Kit
Rutan Aircraft Factory Mojave, California	Vari-Eze

Kit Manufacturer	Model
Sorrell Aviation Tenino, Washington	Hiperbipe Model SNS-7
Stoddard Hamilton Company Maple Valley, Washington	SH-2
Swallow Aero Plane Company Rockfall, Connecticut	Model 2
Ultra Systems, Incorporated Salt Lake City, Utah	Weedhooper J24 Aircraft Construction Kit
Zenair Corporation Richmond Hills Ontario, Canada	CH-200 MC-12 Cricket

The FAA evaluation of amateur aircraft kits is for the purpose of determining eligibility to meet the major portion criteria of FAR 21.191(g) and should not be construed to mean that the amateur aircraft kits are FAA "certificated", or "approved".

APPENDIX 3

SAMPLE NOTARIZED STATEMENT

AMATEUR BUILDER'S NAME ______________________________

ADDRESS ______________________________

CITY ______________ STATE ______________ ZIP ______________

TELEPHONE NO. RESIDENCE ______________ BUSINESS ______________

AIRCRAFT INFORMATION

MODEL ______________ ENGINE(s) MAKE ______________

ASSIGNED SERIAL NO. ______________ ENGINE(s) SERIAL NO. ______________

REGISTRATION NO. ______________ PROPELLER(s) MAKE ______________

AIRCRAFT FABRICATED: PLAN /_/ KIT /_/ PROPELLER(s) SERIAL NO. ______________

STATEMENT

I have fabricated and assembled the major portion of the aforementioned aircraft for my education and/or recreation and have evidence to support this statement available to the FAA upon request.

____
SIGNATURE OF BUILDER

NOTARIZATION STATEMENT:

Appendix IV

Federal Aviation Advisory Circular 61-84 Role of Preflight Preparation

U.S. Department of Transportation

Federal Aviation Administration

Advisory Circular

Subject: ROLE OF PREFLIGHT PREPARATION **Date:** 3/18/85 **Initiated by:** AFO-840 **AC No:** 61-84B **Change:**

1. PURPOSE. This advisory circular (AC) modifies and updates the flight information available to pilots as a result of changes in the basic Airmen Information Manual format.

2. CANCELLATION. AC 61-84A dated December 1, 1980, is canceled.

3. BACKGROUND.

a. One of the most often neglected acts of a pilot contemplating flight in an aircraft is that of proper preflight planning. While the reasons remain obscure, the facts are well supported by aircraft accident statistics. Although the number of general aviation accidents has shown a downward trend in recent years, the accident and fatality/serious injury statistics indicate an increase in the percentage of accidents during takeoff.

b. Statistics taken from the National Transportation Safety Board files show that from 1979 through 1983, 728 persons died and 665 were seriously injured in 4,291 takeoff accidents. These accidents are significant to general aviation pilots--annually, they represent about 20 percent of all general aviation accidents and about 16 percent of all fatalities and serious injuries. Traditionally, pilots have emphasized the planning of the en route and approach/landing phases of flight; e.g., the route to be taken, en route and destination weather, en route and terminal facilities, applicable altitudes and fuel requirements. Accident data, however, indicate that too little preparation is made for the actual takeoff of the aircraft. In order for pilots to fulfill their responsibilities to ensure the safety of the entire flight, it is necessary that they have adequate knowledge of elements involved in preflight planning. It is also necessary that they take time to analyze the conditions and study the various factors which would affect the takeoff, en route, and landing phases of flight.

4. KEY ELEMENTS OF PREFLIGHT PLANNING.

a. Charts.

(1) A basic element of preflight preparation requires the use of current navigational charts on which pilots can mentally review their intended route of flight. They may or may not wish to draw a line on the chart representing the true

course. They should, however, review the projected path across the face of the chart for the location of good checkpoints, restricted areas, obstructions, other flight hazards, and suitable airports. For visual flight rule (VFR) pilot planning by either pilotage or dead reckoning, the Sectional Aeronautical Chart is an excellent choice. It is scaled at 1/500,000, or 8 miles to the inch. The physical characteristics of most landmarks, both cultural and geographic, are shown in great detail. The pilot should have little difficulty identifying the selected landmarks along the route of flight. Another popular chart is the World Aeronautical Chart (WAC). The scale of the WAC is 1/1,000,000, or 16 miles to the inch. Many states print aeronautical charts which are excellent for VFR navigation within their state boundaries. The pilot should realize, however, that all of these charts are designed primarily for VFR navigation and contain only limited information concerning radio aids and frequencies. The use of instrument flight rules (IFR) navigational charts for planning pilotage or dead reckoning VFR flights is not desirable for the following reasons:

(i) Many airports used by the VFR pilot are not depicted or listed on the IFR charts.

(ii) Very few geographic or cultural landmarks are provided.

(iii) The pilot should refer to the Airman's Information Manual - Basic Flight Information and Air Traffic Control Procedures (AIM) - for more precise coverage of this information.

(2) Most pilots are reluctant to admit to being disoriented or lost. Being lost can be an embarrassing and sometimes frightening experience. Pilots should carry appropriate and current aeronautical charts on all cross-country flights. The use of outdated charts may result in flights into airport traffic areas, control zones, or other restricted airspace without proper authorization. Having available the information contained in current charts will enhance the pilot's ability to complete the flight with greater confidence, ease, and safety.

b. Route. Since the shortest distance between two points is a straight line, a majority of pilots desire direct routes for most flights. Quite often there are factors that should be considered that may make a direct flight undesirable. Restricted and prohibited areas present obstacles to direct flights. In single-engine aircraft, pilots should give consideration to circumnavigating large, desolate areas. Pilots should also consider the single-engine service ceiling of multiengine aircraft when operating over high altitude terrain since the terrain elevation may be higher than the single-engine service ceiling of the multiengine aircraft being flown. An example of this is a multiengine aircraft with a single-engine service ceiling of 6,000 feet being flown over terrain of 9,000 feet elevation. Pilots should be aware that the only advantage they may have over a pilot flying a single-engine aircraft may be a wider latitude in selecting a suitable forced landing area.

c. Airman's Information Manual - Basic Flight Information and Air Traffic Control Procedures (AIM). Part 91 of the Federal Aviation Regulations (FAR) states, in part, that each pilot in command shall, before beginning a flight, become familiar with all available information concerning that flight. The AIM contains information concerning cross-country flight and basic fundamentals required for safe flight in the U.S. National Airspace System.

d. Airport/Facility Directory. The Airport/Facility Directory, published by the National Ocean Service, lists airports, seaplane bases, and heliports open to the public, communications data, navigational facilities, and certain special notices such as parachute jumping, Flight Service Station (FSS)/National Weather Service (NWS) telephone numbers, preferred routes, and aeronautical chart bulletins.

e. Notices to Airmen (Class II).

(1) Notices to Airmen (Class II) is issued biweekly and is divided into two sections. The first section contains those notices which are expected to remain in effect for at least 7 days after the effective date of the publication. National Flight Data Center (FDC) Notices to Airmen (NOTAMS) primarily reflect changes to standard instrument approach procedures. FDC NOTAMS also establish flight restrictions and correct data on aeronautical charts.

(2) The second section contains special notices that, either because they are too long or because they concern a wide or unspecified geographical area, are not suitable for inclusion in the first section. The content of these notices vary widely and there are no specific criteria for inclusion, other than their enhancement of flight safety.

f. Notices to Airmen (NOTAM). In addition to NOTAM information contained in the Notices to Airmen (Class II) publication, pilots should check with the nearest FSS for an update on the latest NOTAMS.

g. International Flight Information Manual. The International Flight Information Manual is published quarterly for use of private flyers, businessmen, and nonscheduled operators as a preflight and planning guide for flights outside the United States.

h. International Notices to Airmen.

(1) The International Notices to Airmen is a biweekly publication containing significant international NOTAM information and special notices which may affect a pilot's decision to enter or use certain areas of foreign or international airspace.

(2) Pilots should avail themselves of all appropriate charts and publications, including the AIM and NOTAMS.

i. Weather. A weather briefing is an important part of preflight planning. An overview of the synoptic situation and general weather conditions can be obtained from public media (radio, TV, etc.) or by telephone from recorded sources. This will help the pilot to better understand the overall weather picture when obtaining a complete briefing from the FSS, NWS, or other organization that provides this service. Information on public media and recorded weather sources is contained in the Meteorology chapter of the AIM. This chapter also provides information on how to obtain a complete weather briefing, what to look for, and what to ask of the briefer to ensure that the pilot has all the weather necessary for the flight. The weather information should be weighed very carefully in considering the go/no-go decision. This decision is the sole responsibility of the pilot and compulsion should never take the place of good judgment.

j. Navigation Log. Precise flight planning of log items, such as pre-computed courses, time and distance, navigational aids, and frequencies to be used will make en route errors in these items less likely. Special attention should be given to fuel requirements, keeping in mind the need for an ample reserve as well as location of refueling points available as the flight progresses.

k. Flight Plan (VFR). This is not required by FAR, but is dictated by good operating practice. A flight plan not only assures prompt search and rescue in the event the aircraft becomes overdue or missing, but it also permits the destination station to render better service by having prior knowledge of your flight. It costs only a few minutes of time to file a flight plan and may be the best investment the pilot ever makes.

l. Aircraft Manual. Aircraft manuals contain operating limitations, performance, normal and emergency procedures, and a variety of other operational information for the respective aircraft. Traditionally, aircraft manufacturers have done considerable testing to gather and substantiate the information in the aircraft manual. Pilots should become familiar with the manual and be able to refer to it for information relative to a proposed flight.

5. KEY ELEMENTS DURING TAKEOFF PHASE. The importance of thorough preflight preparation which considers possible hazards to takeoff cannot be over-emphasized. The following elements, which should be carefully considered, continue to emerge as factors in takeoff accidents:

a. Gross Weight.

(1) Maximum allowable gross weight is established for an aircraft as an operating limitation for both safety and performance considerations. The gross weight is important because it is a basis for determining the takeoff distance. If gross weight increases, the takeoff speed must be greater to produce the greater lift required for takeoff. The takeoff distance varies with the square of the gross weight. As an example, for an aircraft with a relatively high thrust-to-weight ratio, a 10 percent increase in takeoff gross weight would cause:

(i) a 5 percent increase in speed necessary for takeoff velocity;

(ii) at least a 9 percent decrease in acceleration; and,

(iii) at least a 21 percent increase in takeoff distance.

NOTE: For aircraft with relatively low thrust-to-weight ratios, the figures are slightly higher.

(2) Operations within the proper gross weight limits are outlined in each operator's manual. Gross weight and center of gravity (CG) limits should be considered during preflight preparation. Weight in excess of the maximum certificated gross weight may be a contributing factor to an accident, especially when coupled with other factors which adversely affect the ability of an aircraft to take off and climb safely. These factors may range from field elevation of the airport to the condition of the runway. The responsibility for considering these factors before each flight rests with the pilot.

b. Balance.

(1) A pilot must not only determine the takeoff weight of the aircraft, but also must assure that the load is arranged to fall within the allowable CG limits for the aircraft. Each aircraft manual provides instructions on the proper method for determining if the aircraft loading meets the balance requirements. The pilot should routinely determine the balance of the aircraft since it is possible to be within the gross weight limits and still exceed the CG limits.

(2) An airplane which exceeds the forward CG limits places heavy loads on the nosewheel and, in conventional landing gear airplanes, may, during braking, cause an uncontrollable condition. Furthermore, performance may be significantly decreased and the stall speed may be much higher.

(3) An airplane loaded in a manner that the CG exceeds the aft limit will have decreased static and dynamic longitudinal stability. This condition can produce sudden and violent stall characteristics and can seriously affect recovery.

(4) Pilots exceeding CG limits in helicopters may experience insufficient cyclic controls to safely control the helicopter. This can be extremely critical while hovering downwind with the helicopter load exceeding the forward CG limit.

c. Ice and Frost.

(1) Ice or frost can affect the takeoff performance of an aircraft significantly. Pilots should never attempt takeoffs with any accumulation of ice or frost on their aircraft. Most pilots are aware of the hazards of ice on the wings of an aircraft. The effects of a hard frost are much more subtle. This is due to an increased roughness of the surface texture of the upper wing and may cause up to a 10 percent increase in the airplane stall speed. It may also require additional speed to produce the lift necessary to become airborne.

(2) Once airborne, the airplane could have an insufficient margin of airspeed above stall such that gusts or turning of the aircraft could result in a stall. Accumulation of ice or frost on helicopter rotor blades results in potential rotor blade stalls at slower forward air speeds. It could also result in an unbalanced rotor blade condition which could cause an uncontrollable vibration.

d. Density Altitude.

(1) Aircraft instruments are calibrated to be correct under one set of conditions. Standard conditions represent theoretical sea level conditions, 59 degrees Farenheit and 29.92 in Hg. As higher elevations are reached, both temperature and pressure normally decrease. Thus, density altitude is determined by compensating for pressure and temperature variances from the standard conditions. A pilot must remember that as density altitude increases, there is a corresponding decrease in the power delivered by the engine and the propellers or rotor blades. For airplanes, this may cause the required takeoff roll to increase by up to 25 percent for every 1,000 feet of elevation above sea level. The most critical conditions of takeoff performance are the result of a combination of heavy loads, unfavorable runway conditions, winds, high temperatures, high airport elevations, and high humidity.

(2) The proper accounting for the pressure altitude (field elevation is a poor substitute) and temperature is mandatory for accurate prediction of takeoff data. The required information will be listed in the aircraft manual and should be consulted before each takeoff, especially if operating at a high density altitude or with a heavily loaded aircraft.

e. Effect of Wind.

(1) Every aircraft manual gives representative wind data and corresponding ground roll distances. A headwind which is 10 percent of the takeoff airspeed will reduce the no-wind takeoff distance by 19 percent. A tailwind which is 10 percent of the takeoff airspeed, however, will increase the no-wind takeoff distance by about 21 percent.

(2) Although this consideration is basic to a successful takeoff, the number of accidents involving the selection of the wrong runway for the existing wind and taking off into unfavorable wind conditions indicates a need for many pilots to reevaluate their preflight planning to ensure that the effect of wind is considered fully.

f. Runway Condition.

(1) There are more than 14,700 airports in the United States, each with runways having various surface compositions, slopes, and degrees of roughness. Takeoff acceleration is affected directly by the runway surface condition and, as a result, it must be a primary consideration during preflight planning.

(2) Most aircraft manuals list takeoff data for level, dry, hard-surfaced runways. The runway to be used, however, is not always hard-surfaced and level. Consequently, pilots must be aware of the effect of the slope or gradient of the runway, the composition of the runway, and the condition of its surface. Each of these can contribute to a failure to obtain/maintain a safe flying speed.

(3) The effective runway gradient is the maximum difference in the runway centerline elevation divided by the runway length. The FAA recognizes the effect of runway gradient on the takeoff roll of an aircraft and has published limits on the maximum gradients. For general aviation VFR airports the maximum longitudinal runway grade is 2 percent and the longitudinal runway grade change is 2 percent maximum. Furthermore, the takeoff length for a runway must be increased an additional 20 percent for each 1 percent of change in effective gradient to a maximum allowable effective gradient change of 2 percent.

(4) Since the runway gradient has a direct bearing on the component weight of the aircraft, a runway gradient of 1 percent would provide a force component along the path of the aircraft which is 1 percent of gross weight. In the case of an upslope, the additional drag and rolling friction caused by a 1 percent upslope can result in a 2 percent to 4 percent increase in the takeoff distance and subsequent climb.

(5) Frequently, the only runway at an airport has a slope. When determining which direction to use for takeoff, pilots must remember that a

direction uphill, but into a headwind, is generally preferred to a downwind takeoff on a downsloping runway. Factors such as steep slope, light wind, etc., however, make an uphill takeoff impractical.

(6) It is difficult to predict the retarding effect on the takeoff run that water, snow/slush, sand, gravel, mud, or long grass on a runway will have, but these factors can be critical to the success of a takeoff. Since the takeoff data in the aircraft manual is predicated on a dry, hard surface each pilot must develop individual guidelines for operations from other type surfaces.

g. Cold Weather Takeoffs. The following is an excerpt taken from AC 91-13C, Cold Weather Operation of Aircraft:

"Takeoffs in cold weather offer some distinct advantages, but they also offer special problems. A few points to remember are:

"(1) Do not overboost supercharged or turbine engines. Use the applicable power charts for the pressure altitude and ambient temperature to determine the appropriate manifold pressure or engine pressure ratio. Care should be exercised in operating normally aspirated engines. Power output increases at about 1 percent for each ten degrees of temperature below that of standard air. At -40 degrees F, an engine might develop 10 percent more than rated power even though RPM and MP limits are not exceeded.

"(2) On multiengine aircraft it must be remembered that the critical engine-out minimum control speed (Vmc) was determined at sea level with a standard day temperature. Therefore, Vmc will be higher than the published figure during a cold weather takeoff unless the power setting is adjusted to compensate for the lower density altitude.

"(3) With reciprocating engines, use carburetor heat as required. In some cases, it is necessary to use heat to vaporize the fuel. Gasoline does not vaporize readily at very cold temperatures. Do not use carburetor heat in such a manner that it raises the mixture temperature to freezing or just a little below. In such cases, it may be inducing carburetor icing. An accurate mixture temperature gauge is a good investment for cold weather operation. On some occasions in extremely cold weather, it may be advisable to use carburetor heat on takeoff.

"(4) If icing conditions exist, use the anti-ice and deice equipment as outlined in the Airplane Flight Manual. If the aircraft is turbine powered, use the appropriate power charts for the condition, bearing in mind that the use of bleed air will, in most cases, affect the aircraft's performance."

6. SUMMARY. Preflight preparation is the foundation of safe flying. Accident statistics of recent years indicate that adequate preflight preparation is lacking in many cases. As a result, while the number of general aviation accidents and approach and landing accidents has declined, takeoff accidents have increased. Statistics indicate that takeoff accidents occur because elements of the preflight preparation were:

a. not assigned the proper importance,

b. not incorporated into the preflight routine, or

c. pilots did not anticipate potential takeoff emergencies and the required procedures to follow.

7. RECOMMENDATION. To enhance the safety of flying, pilots are encouraged to:

a. form good preflight planning habits and review them continually,

b. be thoroughly knowledgeable of the hazards and conditions which would represent potential dangers, particularly during takeoff, and,

c. be aware of the capabilities and limitations of their aircraft.

William T. Brennan
Acting Director of Flight Operations

Glossary

acknowledgment—The act of having a document certified by an officer of the court or by notary public that it contains the signature of the person or party making or signing the document.

actual damages—Damages awarded for injuries or damages actually sustained.

Administrator—The Federal Aviation Administrator or any person to whom he/she has delegated his/her authority in the matter concerned.

adverse—Opposing claim; conflicting; contrary to.

air carrier—A person who undertakes directly by lease or other arrangement to engage in air transportation for commercial reasons.

aircraft—Any device that is used or intended to be used for flight in air.

aircraft engine—An engine that is used or intended to be used in propelling aircraft. It includes any engine appurtenances and accessories necessary for its functioning, but does not include the propeller.

airframe—The fuselage, booms, nacelles, cowlings, fairings, airfoil surfaces (including rotors but excluding propellers and rotating airfoils of engines), and landing gear of an aircraft and their accessories and controls.

appeal—An application to a higher court to change the holding of the lower court.

appellant—The person who makes the appeal to the higher court.

appellee—The person or party against whom an appeal is taken.

argument—The process of reasoning or the discussion of legal points by an attorney.

assign—The act of transferring property or property rights and interests to another.

bond—A written acknowledgment of a debt.

breach of contract—The breaking or violation of the terms of a contract.

capacity—The legal ability to contract, convey property, or make a will.

chattel mortgage—The transfer of title to personal property as security for a debt or the purchase price.

claim—The assertion of a right or demand.

clear title—A title free of any adverse claims of ownership.

cloud on title—An adverse claim or irregularity as shown by the documents on file concerning the item in question.

common law—The general underlying principles of law as recognized by the common law states.

conditional sales—Sales in which the transfer of title depends upon the performance of conditions made a part of the sale.

conflict of laws—The differences between the laws of two states relating to the subject matter of a legal issue.

constructive notice—Implied notice by law, though not necessarily actual notice; documents on file are considered constructive notice if properly filed.

contract—An agreement between two or more parties to do or abstain from doing some act or acts.

conveyance—The transfer of property from one to another.

creditor—One who gives credit to a debtor.

default—Failure to perform a duty or obligation that one has.

document—A deed, agreement, letter, or other writing used to prove or show proof of some fact.

escrow—A delivery of an object or document to a third person or party to hold until both parties to the transaction have performed certain conditions.

Federal District Courts—United States Courts of Record established and holding sessions within established judicial districts of the United States.

Federal Register—A journal published by the federal government which contains notice of federal proclamations, orders, notices, and other documents published by the agencies of the federal government.

filed—Deposited with the proper office as required by law, or custom, referring to a copy or a document.

finding—The decision of a court or jury as to any issues before it.

flight crew member—A pilot, flight engineer, or flight navigator assigned to duty in an aircraft during flight time.

glider—Heavier-than-air aircraft that is supported in flight by the dynamic reaction of the air against its lifting surfaces and whose free flight does not depend principally on an engine.

grant—A generic term used in conveyances; to give or to sell.
gross—Excessive; entire.
gross negligence—High degree of inattention: extreme carelessness.
gyroplane—A rotorcraft whose rotors are normally engine-driven for takeoffs, hovering, and landing and for forward flight through part of its speed range and whose means of propulsion, consisting of conventional propellers, is independent of the rotor system.

helicopter—A rotorcraft that, for its horizontal motion, depends principally on its engine-driven rotors.
holder—One in possession of.

insurance—A contract whereby one party agrees to pay for any loss of property or injuries or claims against the other party in consideration for premiums received.

jurisdiction—The power of a court to retain and decide any issue or matter in dispute.
justification—The showing of sufficient reason for either doing or failing to do some act.

liability—A debt or responsibility; an obligation to pay for damages or injuries to other people or property.
license—Authority or permission to do something which without such permission would be either wrongful or otherwise illegal.
lien—A right in one person to retain the property of another until an obligation owed by the other party to the holder is performed.

material fact—One which in an application for insurance would influence the insurance company in issuing the policy or determining the premium rates.
mechanic's lien—A statutory lien that a mechanic, supplier, or other worker has on the specific property that he has possession of and has either repaired or improved. This lien exists to insure repayment for the work accomplished on the specific property only.
misfeasance—A negligent act.
mortgage—The conveyance of property to a person to secure performance of certain conditions usually involving the repayment of a debt.

negligence—The want of care; ordinary negligence is lack or want of ordinary diligence; slight negligence is negligence of a lesser degree than ordinary; for definition of gross negligence, see *gross negligence*.
notary public—An officer authorized to administer oaths and take acknowledgments.

obligations—That which a person is bound to do as a result of law or agreement that he has entered into.
order—A mandate or demand issued by a court of law.

party—A person, company, or group of people who take part in a legal transaction. Thus the buyer and seller would be parties to a sales contract.

passenger—One who is being transported and who does not perform a function as crew member or pilot.

presumption—A conclusion of law or fact drawn from the proved existence of some other fact; that which is inferred.

public policy—A principle of law that holds that no one may do that which has a tendency to harm the public.

purchaser for value—One who buys property and pays an adequate price for the property as opposed to a gift or grossly low price.

reasonable care—The standard of conduct that a reasonable person would use under the circumstances.

regular on its face—A document which is in the correct format and contains nothing on its face to apprise anyone that it was issued without authority.

release—The act of giving up a claim or interest or right of action.

sale—The transfer of a legal right or interest in property.

standard policy—A form of insurance policy widely used in the United States.

statute—A written law adopted by a unit of government; must be adopted by legislative bodies.

statutory—Depending on an express law, in lieu of common law.

tender—The offer to perform an obligation that one has under a contract.

tort—Injury or wrong to a person.

tort-feasor—One who commits the wrong.

transfer—The act of passing from one to another; a conveyance.

void—Of no force, no effect.

voidable—An imperfect obligation capable of being voided by one of the parties.

warranty—A guarantee concerning property given or implied by the seller to the buyer.

writ—A judicial order for a person or persons to appear before a named judge at a given time.

Index

Index